Royal College of Physicians

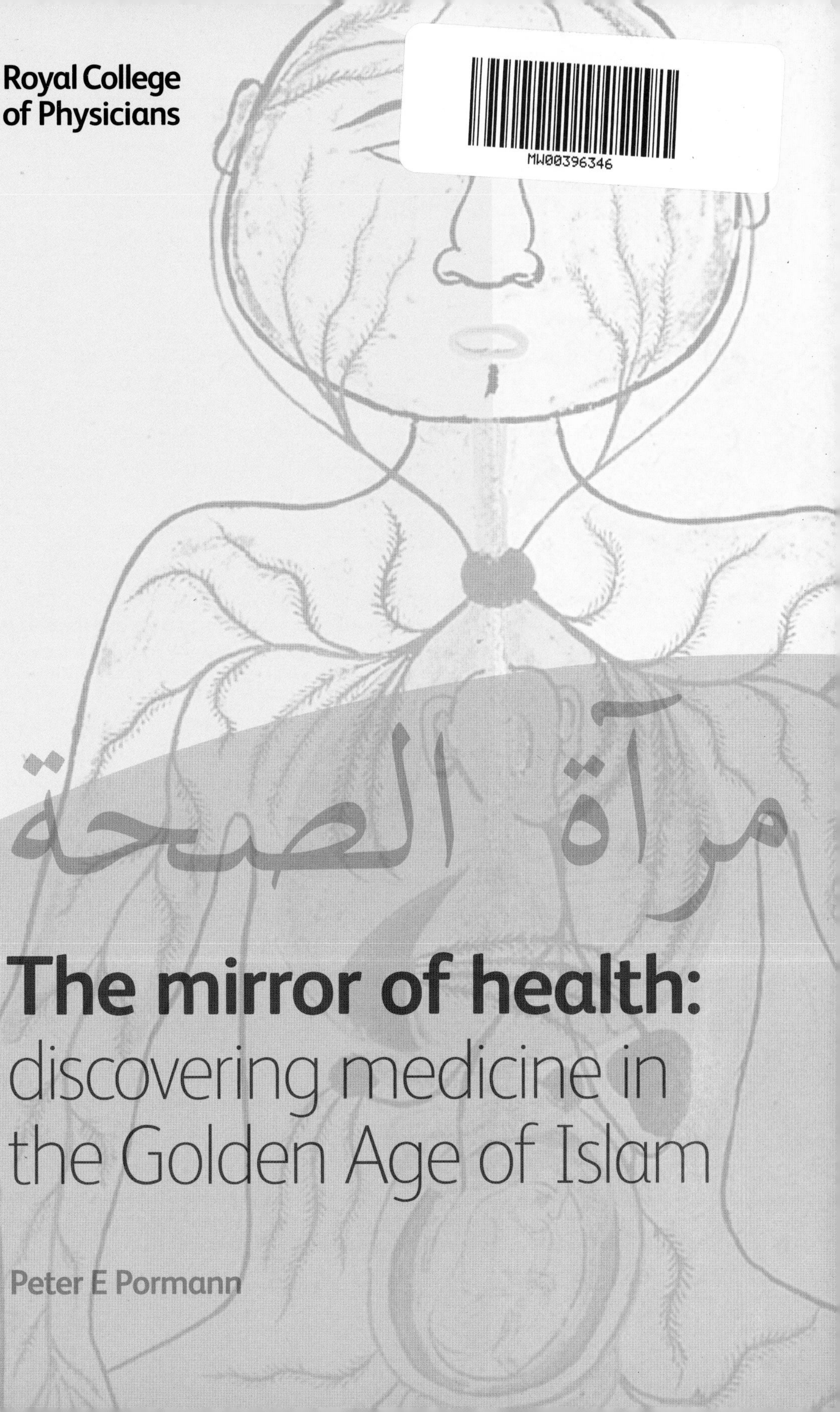

مرآة الصحة

The mirror of health:
discovering medicine in the Golden Age of Islam

Peter E Pormann

The Royal College of Physicians

The Royal College of Physicians is the oldest medical college in England, founded by royal charter of Henry VIII in 1518. The library, archive and museum collections are the product of centuries of gift-giving by RCP fellows and members. The institutional archives contain a wealth of material from the founding charter to 20th century reports on the effects of smoking.

Citation for this document: Pormann PE. *The mirror of health: discovering medicine in the Golden Age of Islam*. London: Royal College of Physicians, 2013.

Acknowledgements

Fig 0.1 was reproduced by courtesy of the University Librarian and Director, The John Rylands Library, The University of Manchester. Figure 1.3 was reproduced by permission of the Provost and Fellows of Eton College. Figures 3.2b, 3.3b and 3.4b were reproduced by permission of the Master and Fellows of Gonville and Caius College, University of Cambridge. Figures 3.2c, 3.3c, 3.4c and 3.5b were reproduced by permission of The Bodleian Library, University of Oxford. Figures 4.1, 6.3, 7.4 and 7.5 were reproduced by permission of the Science Museum, Science & Society Picture Library.

ISBN 978 1 86016 510 8
eISBN 978 1 86016 511 5

Royal College of Physicians
11 St Andrews Place
Regent's Park
London NW1 4LE

www.rcplondon.ac.uk

Registered Charity No 210508

Produced by the Corporate Communications and Publishing Department, Royal College of Physicians
Printed in Great Britain by Charlesworth Press, Wakefield, West Yorkshire

Cover illustration: Female reproductive system, illustration from *Manṣūr's anatomy* (*Tašrīḥ-i Manṣūrī*), 1658.

Contents

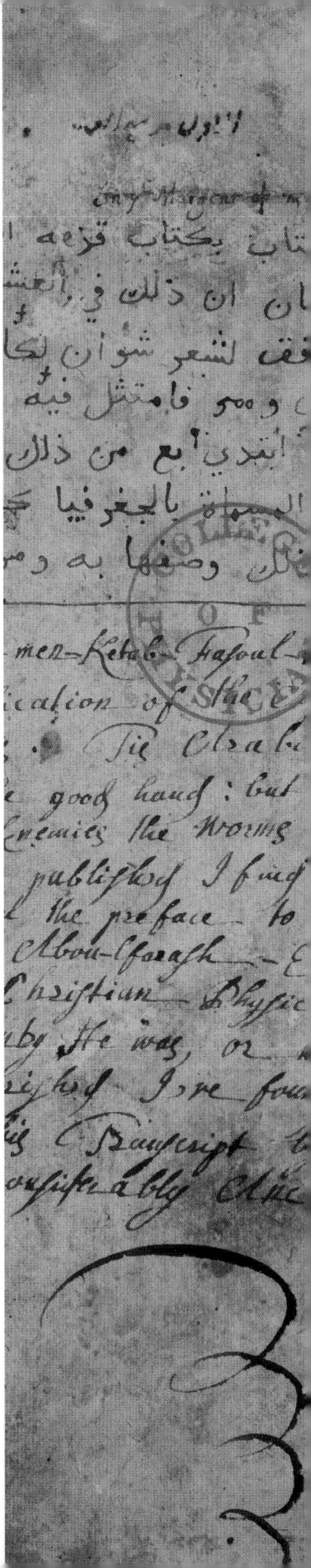

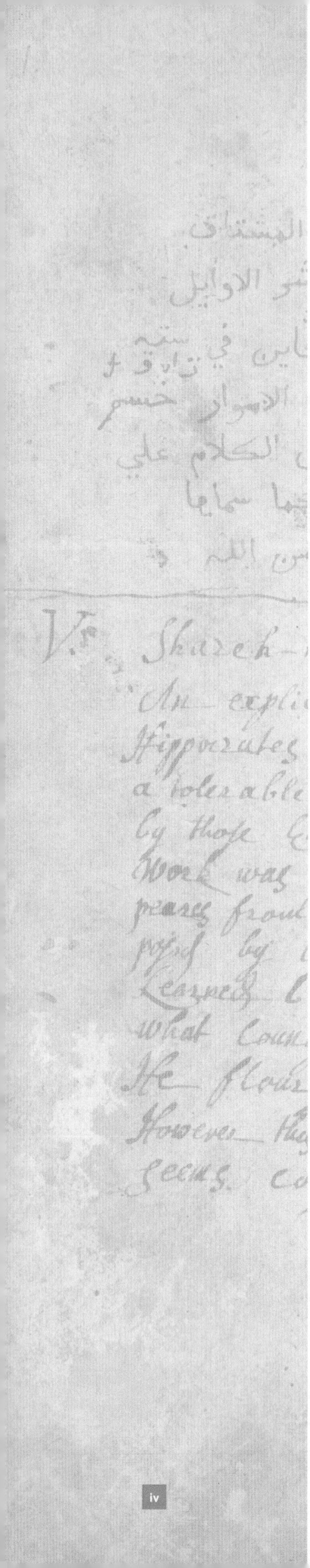

Foreword

The archive collections at the Royal College of Physicians (RCP) are the product of centuries of meticulous recording of College business by officers and fellows. The tradition of formal record-keeping began with President John Caius (1510–73), who compiled the first minute book in 1555, using surviving documents to reconstruct College activities back to the institution's foundation in 1518. This rich history continues and the archives provide a complete picture of RCP life over nearly five centuries.

In addition to institutional records, many RCP members and fellows donated papers on medical and non-medical topics, with manuscripts dating from the 13th century onwards on astrology, alchemy, religion, travel, botany and mathematics, among others. These form an unparalleled resource on the history of medicine and medical education in England and Europe.

Many members and fellows collected works on medicine and medical practice from other cultures, enriching the archives with texts from the Middle East and Asia. During the 1950s, all Arabic and Persian manuscripts were combined as the 'Tritton' collection, named after Arthur Stanley Tritton (1881–1973), professor of Arabic at the School of Oriental and African Studies, London, who catalogued the volumes. This fascinating collection was conserved and researched between 2010 and 2012, inspiring this publication as well as providing the focus of the RCP's 2013 exhibition, *The mirror of health*.

The mirror of health highlights the value the RCP has placed on Islamic medical work and collaborations over five centuries but, more broadly, this seminal work reflects one aspect of the importance to the RCP of its international fellowship and connections. I particularly wish to thank both Professor Pormann for his scholarly presentation of the Islamic medical collection and Pamela Forde, the RCP archive manager, for her outstanding support in bringing this project to fruition.

Linda M Luxon *May 2013*
Treasurer, Royal College of Physicians

Preface

We view ourselves and others reflected in the mirror, but sometimes we need the mirror to see ourselves in others, to perceive the similarities that we share with those around us. When we look deep into the medical tradition of the Islamic lands, we recognise many reflections and refractions: the theory of the four humours, inherited from the Greeks; the figures of Hippocrates and Galen, of Avicenna and Rhazes, and of Vesalius. But why the great Renaissance anatomist Vesalius? Because so much of European university medicine in the pre-modern period is anchored in the Arabic tradition.

Islamic culture flourished under the ʿAbbāsid dynasty, from the time it seized power in the 750s to the sack of Baghdad by the Mongols in 1258. Then came the age of decline, or so the story goes. This book tells a different tale. Medicine and medical care continued well beyond the sack of Baghdad, and spread not only through the heartlands of the Islamic empires, but also to its periphery. The exchange of ideas between East and West is not limited to the famous translation movement of 9th-century Baghdad, a fertile intellectual environment rightly compared to Classical Greece and Renaissance Italy. It continued, for instance, at the Ottoman court in the 17th century. Physicians kept discovering new things in the 13th century and later, as we shall see. So if there was a Golden Age, it extended well beyond its traditional temporal confines.

This book will take the reader on a journey across the Mediterranean and through time to discover the medicine of distant cultures: medicine which often turns out to resemble our own. It tells a fascinating story about the transmission and translation of scientific knowledge: members of different countries and creeds take part in one scientific discourse to further the Art. On the basis of the old, they invent the new. They test, refine, reflect, criticise, debate, discuss and, at times, dismiss the work of their forebears to improve human health.

Peter E Pormann *May 2013*
Director of the John Rylands Research Institute,
Professor of classics and Graeco-Arabic studies,
The University of Manchester

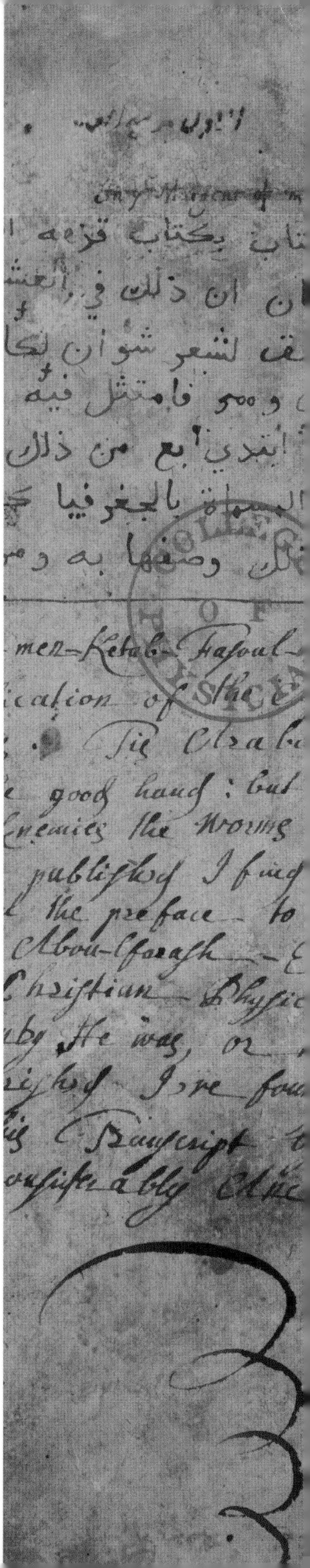

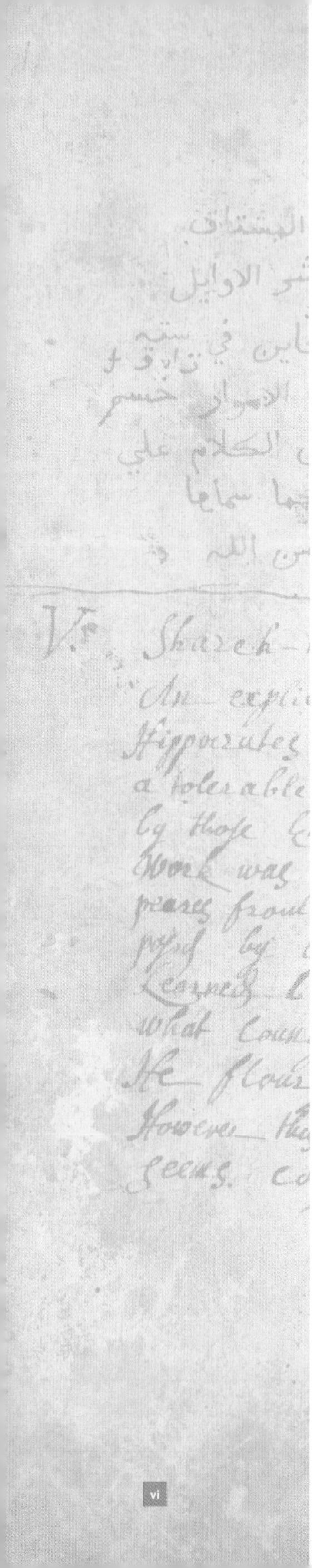

Introduction to the Royal College of Physicians' collections

The first Islamic medical manuscripts to enter the collections of the Royal College of Physicians (RCP) were presented by John Selden (1584–1654), a prominent lawyer, historian and linguistic scholar. He bequeathed 11 oriental medical manuscripts to the RCP on 9 April 1655 and 1 Feb 1655/6; another RCP fellow, Dr William Rant (1604–53), donated six Arabic books at the same time. Selden was also responsible for the 1648 acquisition of books from the collection of Isaac Faragi, a Jewish scholar and collector, which included Hebrew and Persian manuscripts, and many printed books.

A second important figure in the collections' history was Henry Wild (1684–1734), the 'Arabian tailor', who grew up in Norwich where he attended a local grammar school. Unable to afford university, he was apprenticed to a tailor and became a journeyman. This did not prevent him from studying in his spare time. Wild attracted the attention of Humphrey Prideaux (1648–1724), the dean of Norwich and author of a *Life of Mahomet* (1697). Prideaux sponsored him to go to Oxford and Wild was admitted to the Bodleian Library.

Around 1720, Wild moved to London under the patronage of Dr Richard Mead (1673–1754), an influential RCP fellow, as well as an accomplished scholar and collector. During his first year in London, he catalogued 10 of the 11 manuscripts donated by Selden, presumably at the request of his new patron.

The Arabic collections also attracted the interest of the orientalist and lexicographer, Edmund Castell (1606–85). He spent a large fortune on printing a heptaglot lexicon (where the text is arranged in seven parallel columns) in Hebrew, Samaritan, Chaldee (ie Aramaic), Syriac, Arabic, Ethiopian and Persian. He used the RCP's oriental collections while researching his lexicon, which was eventually finished in 1669.

The last manuscripts came into the collection in the first half of the 20th century. The most significant donor was Professor Roy Dobbin FRCP (1873–1939), who spent a large part of his career in Cairo, Egypt. He gave 31 manuscripts to the RCP. He avidly collected books and manuscripts, and developed a particular interest in the history of gynaecology and obstetrics among the Arabs.

After Dobbin's death in 1939, Cairo University created a medal in his name and named a gynaecological ward in the hospital after him.

Cyril Elgood (1892–1970), lived in Persia from 1925 to 1931, and is the second most important donor in modern times. He gave 10 oriental manuscripts, as well as one containing his English translation of a Persian medical manual entitled *The mirror of health* (*Mirʾāt al-ṣiḥḥa*), which gives this work, and the accompanying 2013 exhibition, its title. Dobbin and Elgood's scholarly pursuits indicate the two important centres of the Islamic world at that time. Egypt was the cultural and intellectual centre for most Arabs, and Persia, renamed Iran in 1934, remained the focal point of the Persian-speaking world.

In 1950, the RCP decided to catalogue its oriental manuscripts, while taking stock of its holdings in the post-war period. In January 1951, the RCP entrusted Professor Tritton, professor of Arabic at SOAS, with the task. His summary catalogue appeared in the same year in the *Journal of the Royal Asiatic Society*. All Arabic, Persian and Turkish manuscripts still bear the shelf mark assigned by Tritton.

Pamela Forde *May 2013*
Archive manager, Royal College of Physicians

'The most significant donor was Professor Roy Dobbin FRCP (1873–1939), who spent a large part of his career in Cairo, Egypt. He gave 31 manuscripts to the RCP.'

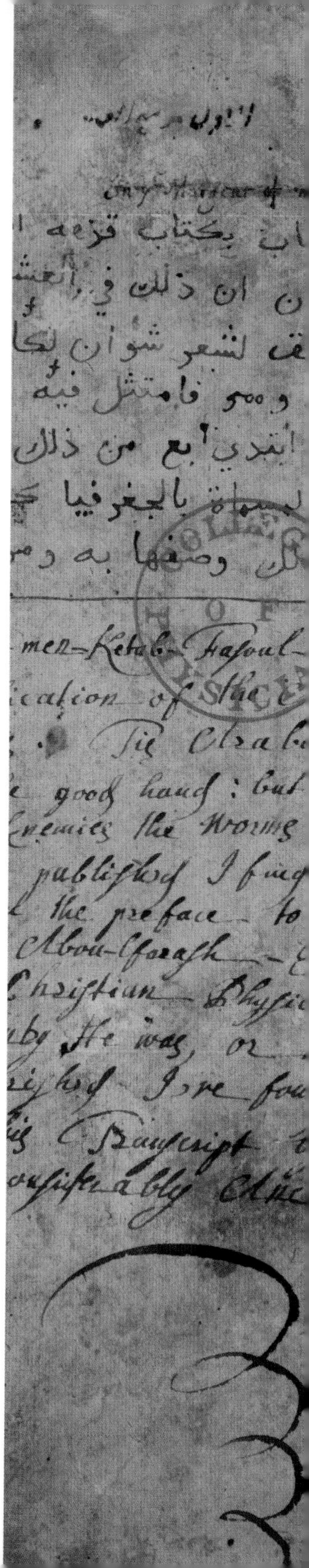

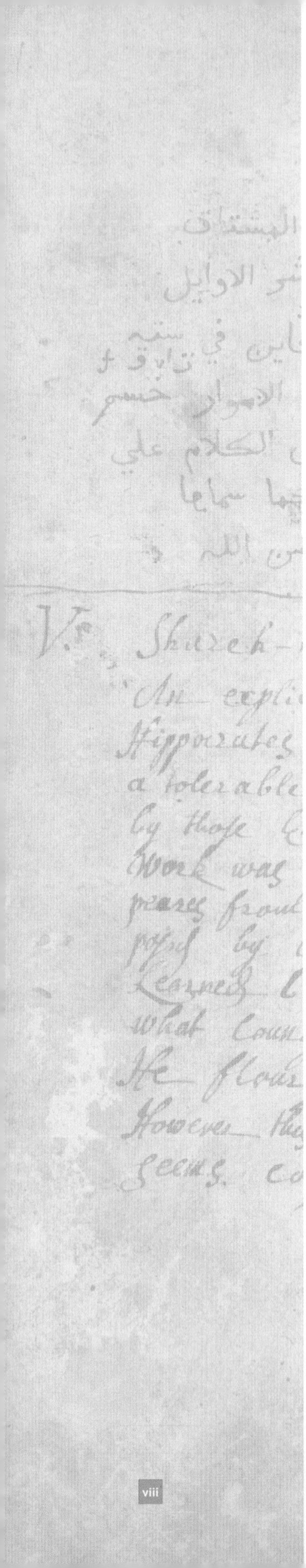

Acknowledgements

Compiling a catalogue of this type is a collective effort. In writing it, I have incurred many debts of gratitude from different quarters, and it is a great pleasure to acknowledge them here. First of all, I would like to thank the RCP for commissioning the project of cataloguing the Arabic, Persian and Turkish manuscripts in its collections, as well as mounting the exhibition, *The mirror of health,* together with this accompanying catalogue. Pamela Forde, the archive manager at the RCP, has supported this project from its inception. Her help is most visible in chapters 8 and 9, but her input pervades this volume. James Partridge, from the Corporate Communications and Publishing Department at the RCP, designed this book and deserves praise for the attractive layout and the meticulous attention to detail (including typesetting in Arabic and Greek). The results of his efforts are not only pleasing to the eye, but also underline the importance of the collection visually.

At Manchester, I benefited from the support of colleagues at the John Rylands Library and in my own research team. John Hodgson, collections and research support manager at the Library, assisted me in numerous ways, and kindly gave permission for a page from one of the Library's early printed books to be reproduced here free of charge. Likewise, the two research associates working on my ERC-funded project 'Arabic commentaries on the Hippocratic aphorisms', Dr Taro Mimura and Dr Emily Selove, shared their respective expertise and offered important suggestions. My administrator, Stevie Spiegl, read most of the manuscript and saved me from many errors.

The Foundation for Science, Technology and Civilisation kindly supported the exhibition. I am grateful to its president, Professor Salim TS Al-Hassani, to Ian Kendrick, its general manager, and to its anonymous referees for the comments that they offered on an earlier draft, as well as their suggestions for improvement. Although I benefited from their advice, there were some points on which we agreed to disagree, and overall our collaboration was both amiable and fruitful.

The libraries and institutions who kindly lent their treasures to the RCP also deserve my thanks. Their curators and staff were equally helpful; they include Dr Bruce C Barker-Benfield and Alisdair Watson, both senior assistant librarians at the Bodleian

Library, Oxford; Mark Statham, college librarian at Gonville and Caius College, Cambridge; and Selina Hurley, assistant curator of medicine at the Science Museum, London.

Among the many other colleagues who lent their expertise, I would like to single out four. Dr Nikolai Serikoff, Asian collections librarian at the Wellcome Library in London, graciously shared his expertise with me. Dr Natalia Bachour, wissenschaftliche Mitarbeiterin at Zurich University, kindly advised me on Ibn Sallūm and the translations of Paracelsian works that he commissioned. Professor Charles Burnett, professor of the history of Islamic influences in Europe at the Warburg Institute, has been supportive in more than one way. Finally, my esteemed teacher Professor Emilie Savage-Smith, professor of the history of Islamic science at Oxford University, helped me, as always, with great liberality.

All these institutions and individuals have my heartfelt gratitude. Yet, although they all kindly shared in this endeavour, the interpretations and analyses that I offer here are my own, and any errors and omissions are also entirely my responsibility.

Peter E Pormann *May 2013*

'Compiling a catalogue of this type is a collective effort. In writing it, I have incurred many debts of gratitude from different quarters, and it is a great pleasure to acknowledge them here ...'

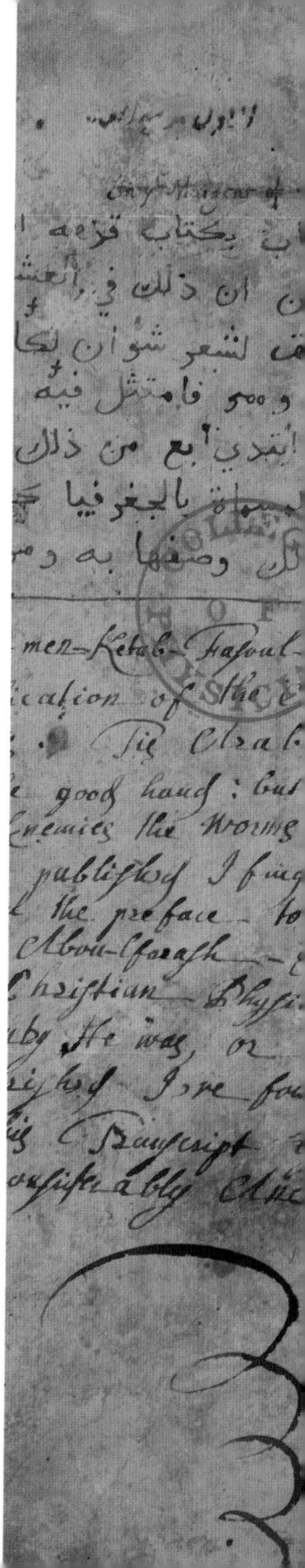

List of illustrations

Illustrations shown in this catalogue are called figures, eg **Fig 1.1**, and items shown in the exhibition are numbered as in the exhibition displays, eg **no 3.** Both are highlighted in bold in the text.

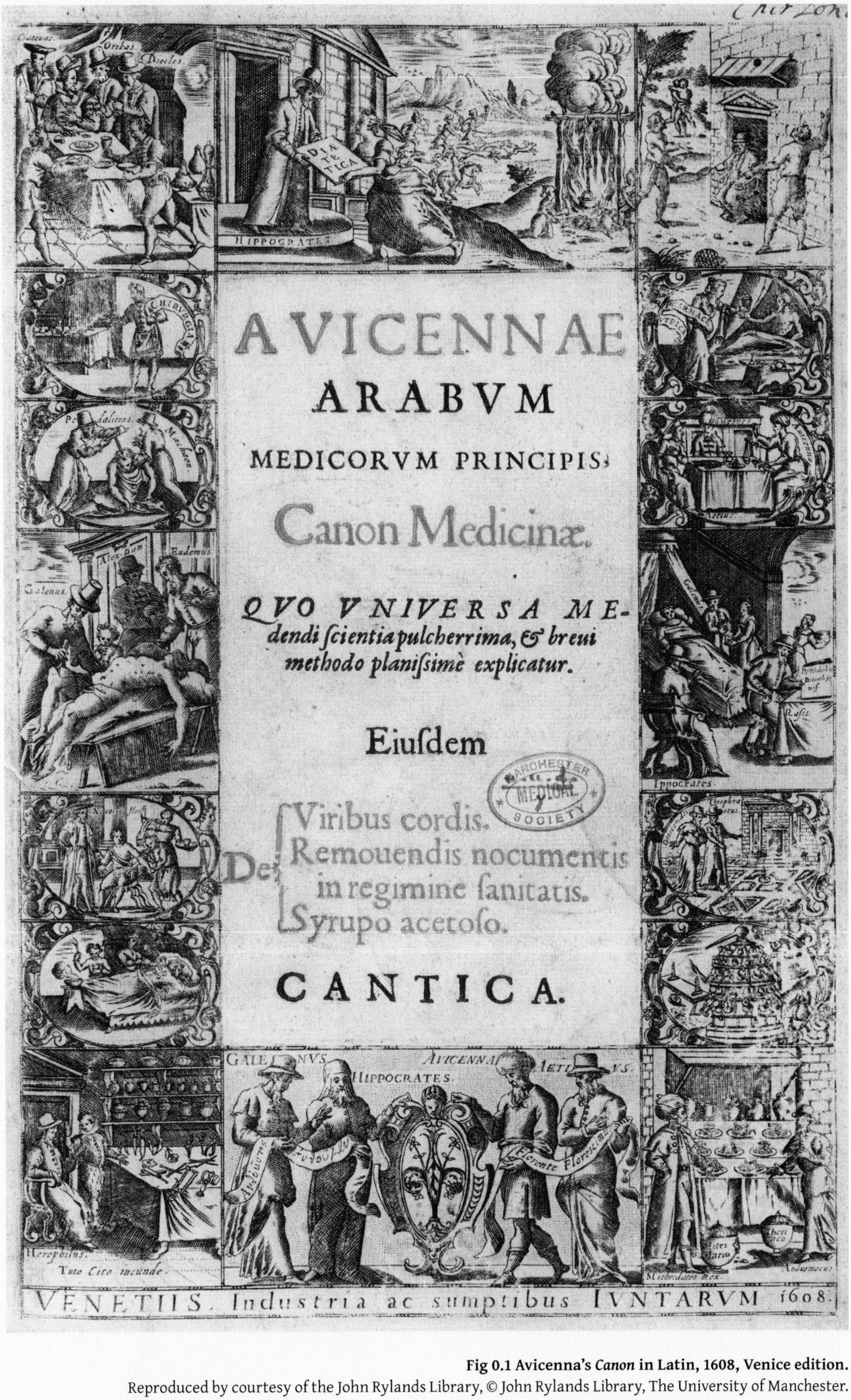

AVICENNAE
ARABVM
MEDICORVM PRINCIPIS;
Canon Medicinæ.

QVO VNIVERSA MEdendi ſcientia pulcherrima, & breui methodo planiſsimè explicatur.

Eiuſdem

De { Viribus cordis.
Remouendis nocumentis in regimine ſanitatis.
Syrupo acetoſo.

CANTICA.

VENETIIS. Induſtria ac ſumptibus IVNTARVM 1608.

Fig 0.1 Avicenna's *Canon* in Latin, 1608, Venice edition.
Reproduced by courtesy of the John Rylands Library, © John Rylands Library, The University of Manchester.

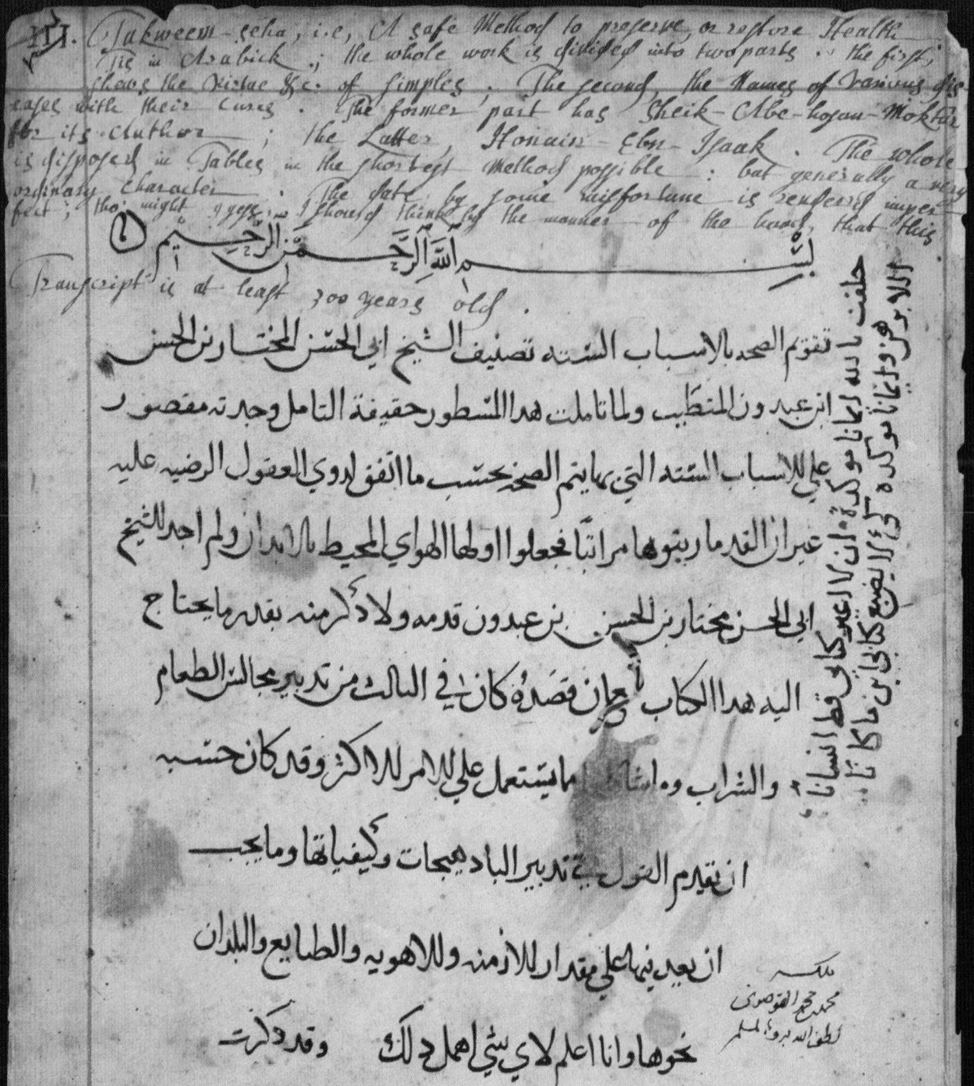

XI. Takweem-seha, i.e. A safe Method to preserve, or restore Health. 'Tis in Arabick; the whole work is divided into two parts: the first shews the Virtue &c. of Simples. The second, the Names of various diseases with their Cures. The former part has Sheik-Abe-hosan-Moktar for its Author; the Latter, Honain-Ebn-Isaak. The whole is disposed in Tables in the shortest Method possible: but generally a very ordinary Character. The date by some misfortune is rendered imperfect; tho' might … I should think by the manner of the hand, that this Transcript is at least 300 years old.

بسم الله الرحمن الرحيم

تقويم الصحة بالاسباب الستة تصنيف الشيخ ابي الحسن المختار بن الحسن
ابن عبدون المتطبب ولما تاملت هذه السطور حقيقة التامل وجدته مقصور
علي الاسباب الستة التي بها يتم الصحة حسب ما اتفق ذوي العقول الرضية عليه
غير ان القدما رتبوها مراتبا فجعلوا اولها الهوا المحيط بالابدان ولم اجد الشيخ
ابي الحسن مختار بن الحسن بن عبدون قدمه ولا ذكر منه بقدر ما يحتاج
اليه هذا الكتاب [illegible] كان في الثالث من تدبير مجالس الطعام
والشراب [illegible] ما يشتمل علي الامر الاكثر وقد كان حسبه
ان يقدم القول في تدبير البادهيجات وكيفياتها وما يجب
ان يعد فيها علي مقدار الازمنة والاهوية والطبايع والبلدان
نحوها وانا اعلم لاي شي اهمل ذلك وقد ذكرت
في اخر هذا الكتاب ما فيه اقناع وكفاية
والحمد لله رب العالمين

Fig 0.2 The opening page of the *Almanac of health* (*Taqwīm al-ṣiḥḥa*) by Ibn Buṭlān (*d* after 1063), with annotations by Henry Wild.

Introduction

The pursuit of health is a fundamental human experience. Many different civilisations have contributed to the development of medicine as a discipline, including those of Ancient Egypt and the Fertile Crescent, on which classical Greek culture drew when developing its own systems of medicine, science and philosophy.

The Islamic civilisation developed a system of healthcare that, at its height, was widely envied. Therefore, medicine evolved into a highly complex discipline from the 7th to the 21st century in the various lands of Islam. Medicine transcended country and creed, as physicians from diverse religious, linguistic and ethnic backgrounds shared in its scientific discourse. Islamic medicine also had a profound impact on surrounding cultures, notably European university medicine as it developed from the 12th century onwards. It survives today, in modified form, in many Muslim countries, and among Muslim communities across the world.

The collections of the Royal College of Physicians (RCP) illustrate in many different ways the dynamism of medical thought and practice in the medieval Islamic world. But they also show that medicine as it developed in Europe from the Middle Ages and the Renaissance onwards is intimately linked to the Arabo-Islamic tradition. Through translation, trade and travel, medical ideas crossed cultural and linguistic bounds and countries' borders to form a shared tradition in which the same authorities – be they Greek or Arabic – dominated the scientific discourse. Examples include Hippocrates, the 'father of medicine', and the great Galen in the Greek tradition; and al-Rāzī and Ibn Sīnā, known as Rhazes and Avicenna in the Latin West, in the Arabic tradition. Both in the early modern and the modern periods, fellows and friends of the RCP took an interest in acquiring oriental manuscripts. Their endeavours to study the Arabic tradition testify to the esteem that it enjoyed. They investigated this tradition mainly for two reasons: as a source for medical knowledge that could inform current clinical practice and as a part of the history of the art that they themselves exercised.

The exhibition and this catalogue are organised around nine themes:

- Galen as the most prominent figure illustrating the Greek legacy in the Arabic tradition and the importance of the Graeco-Arabic translation movement
- Avicenna (or Ibn Sīnā, d 1037) and his legacy both in the East and the West
- the subject of anatomy in the Arabic tradition, with special focus on a historical mystery: the similarity between anatomical illustrations in *Manṣūr's anatomy* and some earlier Latin material
- the clinician and philosopher Abū Bakr Muḥammad ibn Zakarīyāʾ al-Rāzī, known among the Latins as Rhazes (d *c*925)
- the role that magic and divination played in people's reaction to diseases and ill health
- the various methods of therapy used in the Arab world, such as simple and compound drugs, venesection and cupping
- the adoption and adaptation of Paracelsus' new 'chemical medicine' in Ottoman times
- the history of the collection in the Renaissance
- a review of the collection in the 20th century.

At the beginning of each chapter, there will be a short introduction to the theme in question, and how the objects displayed at the RCP relate and reflect aspects of the history of medicine in the medieval Arab world. This thematic approach has the merit of telling interesting stories about patients and practitioners, and about the texts and objects that they employed. The rushed reader can delve into those topics that are of interest or just check on the background of a particular object. Yet this approach does not provide space for a more rounded overview. The rest of this introduction serves to fill this gap. It contains a short essay highlighting the most interesting trends in the history of medieval Islamic medicine. This introduction focuses on the origins of Islamic medicine, and then addresses three thematic complexes: medical theory, medical practice and medicine within a societal context. Rather than a comprehensive list of names and works, it will provide salient examples that can illustrate the innovative and multifaceted nature of Islamic medicine, and its connection to earlier and later medical traditions.

Origins

Islam emerged in the Arabian peninsula. Among its desert-dwelling population, various medical techniques appear to have been known (Pormann 2007a: 77–9). Diseases such as coughing (*suʿāl*) and ophthalmia (*ramad*), and injuries (often caused by tribal warfare) all figured in the pre-Islamic and early Islamic poems. Some Greek instruments were already used such as the probe (Arabic *mīl* from Greek *mḗlē*). Generally speaking, however, cures were often simple – camel urine and honey, for instance, had some prominence.

In the two centuries before the emergence of Islam, the Arabs also came into contact with the two great empires, the Sassanian and the Byzantine, as well as the Syriac-speaking Christians who often had to flee from religious persecution by their coreligionists who declared them to be heretics. All these communities possessed a quite sophisticated medicine, with that of the Greeks clearly standing out among the others. To understand later Islamic developments, it is necessary to get a sense of the medicine that was available in the late antique world.

Alexandria in Egypt rose to prominence in both medicine and philosophy. In its lecture theatres, so-called iatrosophists (or 'professors of medicine') taught the subject from textbooks based on the writings of Hippocrates (fl *c*420s BC) and Galen (*c*129–216); the so-called 'Sixteen books of Galen', a collection of fundamental works, many written by Galen 'for beginners', proved particularly popular (Pormann 2010a). In this way, Galenism was the medical ideology that dominated at the time (Temkin 1973), although some iatrosophists also taught their students at the bedside (Duffy 1984; Scarborough 2010). Two genres of medical literature became particularly important: the commentary and the encyclopaedia. In both commentary and abridgment, medical teachers used the mnemonic technique of *dihaíresis* or division in order to arrange the subject matter in a way that the students could easily grasp and remember (Pormann 2004b). Medical encyclopaedias aimed at presenting the available medical knowledge in an accessible format. The one by Paul of Aegina (fl *c*640s) and later known among the Arabs as *Compendium of the Pleiades* (*Kunnāš al-Ṯurayyā*) exemplifies this genre: in seven books it deals with hygiene, prophylactics and diet (book 1), fevers (book 2), diseases from tip to toe (book 3), external ailments and worms (book 4), poisonous animals (book 5), surgery (book 6), and simple and compound drugs (book 7) (Pormann 2004a).

The Syriac medical tradition, like Syriac literature in general, owed a great debt to the Greek heritage, and notably to the Galenism of late antique Alexandria. Sergius of Rešʿaynā, a Jacobite priest who studied medicine and philosophy in Alexandria, was the most important figure in the pre-Islamic period. He translated many philosophical texts, but also the 'Sixteen books of Galen' (Bhayro 2005; Pormann 2011b). Likewise, the Persian medical tradition owed much to the Greek legacy (Hampel 1982). Syriac-speaking Christians and the medical schools of Alexandrian played a crucial role in one of the greatest enterprises in knowledge transfer: the Graeco-Arabic translation movement (Gutas 1998; Pormann 2010b). Over the course of the 9th century, most available Greek medical texts were translated into Arabic, often via Syriac intermediary translations. The history of the translation movement from Greek into Arabic can be nicely illustrated with the example of Galen's *On simple drugs* (**no 1**), which was twice rendered into Arabic. A certain al-Biṭrīq (fl *c*754–75), about whom little is known, translated the Greek in a rather paraphrastic way, with many of the more technical terms left in transliterations. Fifty years later, Ḥunayn ibn Isḥāq (d *c*873) and his circle had developed a highly refined translational style and further enhanced the medical terminology. When they translated *On simple drugs* into Arabic, they were able to express even extremely complicated medical ideas in sophisticated Arabic (Ullmann 2002, 2006–7; Pormann 2012b). In other words, the technical medical language, that was largely shaped through the translation, had come of age.

Although Greek medical literature, available from the 9th century in Arabic, became the most important source for the development of Islamic medicine, texts from other languages were also rendered into Arabic. For instance, the medical encyclopaedias by the Syriac physician Ibn Sarābiyūn (fl *c*870s) were translated repeatedly into Arabic (Pormann 2004c), and Indian medical lore appears in the *Paradise of wisdom* (*Firdaws al-Ḥikma*) by ʿAlī ibn Rabban al-Ṭabarī (fl *c*850) (Siggel 1951). Trade and travel also played a significant role in the development of Islamic medicine. Not only did new texts become available through the import and export of books, but many previously unknown medicinal substances, such as musk, arrived in the medical marketplace (Akasoy, Yoeli-Tlalim 2007). They were incorporated into the Galenic system of humoral pathology (Pormann 2011b).

Division (*dihaíresis*) was an important principle in late antique Alexandria, and was often also used by Arab and Muslim physicians. For instance, the art of medicine (*ṣināʿat al-ṭibb*) was divided into 'theory' (*ʿilm*) and 'practice' (*ʿamal*). Theory was then subdivided into 'physiology' (*ʿilm al-ṭabāʾiʿ*), 'aetiology' (*ʿilm al-asbāb*) and 'semiotics' (*ʿilm al-ʿalāmāt*), and practice into 'prophylactics' (*ḥifẓ al-ṣiḥḥa*) and 'therapeutics' (*inǧilāb al-ṣiḥḥa*). This division, found, for instance, in the *Alexandrian summaries* (*Ǧawāmiʿ al-Iskandarānīyīn*) on Galen's *On the sect for beginners*, can serve as a guideline for the thematic overview of Islamic medicine (Pormann 2004b).

Medical theory

Physicians and philosophers had different ideas about the place of medicine within the hierarchy of knowledge. For some physicians such as al-Ruhāwī (fl mid-9th century), it was the 'greatest benefit for mankind' (to use an anachronistic expression), the highest and most important science. Others such as Avicenna (Ibn Sīnā, d 1037) relegated it to the status of applied or derivative science, grouping it together with agriculture and astrology (Gutas 2003).

Physiology

The theory known as 'humoral pathology' dominated medical discourse in the Islamic and the European world until the advent of germ theory in the second half of the 19th century. According to humoral pathology, health consists in a balance (*iʿtidāl*) of the four humours – blood (*dam*), phlegm (*balġam*), yellow bile (*mirra ṣafrāʾ*) and black bile (*mirra sawdāʾ*). Each of these four humours has two of the four primary qualities, hot or cold and dry or moist. For instance, black bile is cold and dry, whereas blood is hot and moist. When an imbalance in the four humours occurs, disease ensues. Therapy aims at restoring the balance by removing excessive humours – for instance blood through venesection (*faṣd*; see **no 21**) and cupping (*ḥiǧāma*; see **no 22**) – and regenerating deficient humours – for example, by eating a diet that produces blood or phlegm, and so on.

Following in the footsteps of their Greek forebears, physicians in the medieval Islamic world took an acute interest in anatomy (*tašrīḥ*; see chapter 3). Like the Greek term *anatomḗ*, however, the Arabic *tašrīḥ* was ambiguous, denoting both the study of human physiology (what we nowadays call 'anatomy' in English), and dissection, the 'cutting open' of human and animal bodies, either dead (dissection) or alive (vivisection). Anatomy in the modern sense was a greatly esteemed pursuit. Not only did physicians repeatedly state that students must study it, but theologians such as al-Ġazālī (d 1111) also prized it highly, since it made man understand God's providence (*ʿināyat Allāh*). In other words, the wonderful structure of the human body shows God's intelligent design. Although dissection was not regularly performed, there was no taboo against its practice on human bodies (Savage-Smith 1995). We even have a number of famous cases where Muslim physicians challenge Galenic anatomy. In his commentary on Avicenna's *Canon* (**no 6**), for instance, the physician and philosopher Ibn al-Nafīs (d 1288) discovered the pulmonary transit: the fact that the blood does not pass from the right ventricle of the heart to the left via an opening (*manfaḏ*) in the septum, but rather passes through the lungs (Fancy 2013).

Aetiology

Diseases can have natural and non-natural causes. Natural causes include an imbalance of the humours. The 'six non-naturals', as they were known – the surrounding air, food and drink, sleeping and waking, exercise and rest, retention and evacuation, and the mental state – also affected the health of a person. Too much exercise, for example, could cause excessive heat in the body, which had other physiological consequences; lack of sleep could lead to health problems, and so on. Retention and evacuation refers to the bowel movement and urination of the patient, but could also take other forms such as sexual intercourse, during which semen is evacuated (in both men and women) (Pormann 2007b). The link between mind and body, between mental and physical states, was a strong one. On the one hand, sadness, sorrow, grief, fright and fear could cause bodily reactions leading to disease. On the other hand, mental states were seen as the result of a person's mixture or temperament (*mizāǧ*, Greek *krâsis*). Galen had written a treatise *That the faculties of the soul follow the mixtures of the body*, which was translated into Arabic (Biesterfeldt 1973). The origin of a disease could also be a superfluity (*faḍl*, pl *fuḍūl*) or disease matter (*mādda*, pl *mawādd*). Through digestion, for instance, food is transformed into different humours (most importantly blood). But during this process, certain by-products are also generated. Some are harmless, and are expelled easily from the body, or even have a useful effect. Hair, for instance, is compressed superfluous vapour, excreted through the pores of the skin. Yet other superfluities are harmful, and turn into disease matter, which in its turn provokes an imbalance in the humours of the body (*sūʾ al-mizāǧ*, Greek *duskrasía*).

It is useful to consider a concrete example of how these different factors come together in causing a disease. Melancholy (*malinḫūliyā*) is, as its name suggests, a disease caused by black bile (*al-mirra al-sawdāʾ*, Greek *mélaina cholḗ*). This sounds easy: black bile causes melancholy; melancholy is cured by the removal of black bile. But this example illustrates that the medical theory was far more complex than this facile equation suggests. For melancholy can be innate and acquired. Some people have a natural mixture (*mizāǧ*) that predisposes them for melancholy. The excess of black bile in them, however, does not always lead to an acute illness; only when the black bile in the blood is stirred (eg in the spring) does melancholy ensue. People having this natural predisposition have a whole host of physical features (eg being hairy, having dark skin, lisping, having protruding lips and eyes). Melancholy is acquired in a variety of ways. The wrong food can lead to melancholy, but also the wrong lifestyle, and even mental activities, such as excessive thinking. Moreover, three types of melancholy existed: hypochondriac, encephalic and general. The therapeutic measures to counter the disease ranged from simple and compound drugs, to music, wine and sexual intercourse (see Pormann 2008a, 2012b, 2014; Omrani 2010). Melancholy was only one of many mental disorders for which physicians in the Islamic world developed sophisticated categories and therapies. Moreover, music and hospitals played a particular role in the care of those suffering from mental diseases (Dols 1992).

Semiotics

In order to treat a disease, it was first necessary to diagnose it by recognising its 'signs' (*ʿalāmāt*, sg *ʿalāma*). The complexion (*lawn*), urine (*bawl*) and pulse (*nabaḍ*), for instance, could offer indications (*dalālāt*, sg *dalāla*), allowing the physician to deduce from which disease the patient suffered. Taking the patient's history obviously occupied a prominent place here, and a number of treatises on medical ethics give clear instructions on how the physician should proceed. In this area too Greek texts such as the Hippocratic *Prognostic* (Arabic title: *Fī taqdimat al-maʿrifa*) and Galen's commentary on this work, as well as his own *On prognosis* (*Nawādir taqdimat al-maʿrifa*), offered important guidance. Yet the physicians writing in Arabic were also capable of innovation, going beyond the Greek model. Two famous examples can illustrate this.

Smallpox and measles have similar symptoms such as high fever and rashes or pustules on the skin. The clinician Abū Bakr Muḥammad ibn Zakarīyāʾ al-Rāzī (d *c*925) wrote a major and highly influential treatise *On smallpox and measles* (*Fī al-Ǧudarī wa-l-ḥaṣba*), in which he distinguishes between the two conditions and offers tools for differential diagnosis, a topic on which he also wrote a separate work with the title *What differentiates (between diseases)* (*Kitāb mā l-Fāriq*). *On smallpox and measles* continued to be highly influential not only in the East, but also in Europe, with Latin, English and French translations appearing in the 18th and 19th centuries (**no 16**; Greenhill 1848). In the field of ophthalmology, too, new diseases were discovered and distinguished from previously known ailments, as the example of *sabal* (pannus) shows. This disease, in which blood vessels from the limbus invade the cornea, does not appear in the classical Greek medical works. Yuḥannā ibn Miskawayh and his pupil Ḥunayn ibn Isḥāq, however, included it in their ophthalmological works and advise on its treatment (Savage-Smith 1980; *pace* Savage-Smith 2002).

Medical literature

Books on single topics such as those by al-Rāzī *On smallpox and measles* or Ḥunayn's *Ten treatises on the eye* (*Al-ʿAšr maqālāt fī al-ʿayn*) are monographs and only represent one genre within the medical literature. Ophthalmology as a specialist subject generated many more monographs by authors such as ʿAlī ibn ʿĪsā al-Kaḥḥāl (10th century), ʿAmmār ibn ʿAlī al-Mawṣilī (fl *c*1000) and Ḫalīfa ibn Abī al-Maḥāsin al-Ḥalabī (fl *c*1250s–70s) (Sezgin 1986). Sexual hygiene also evolved into a separate subject with monographs by authors such as al-Kindī, Qusṭā ibn Lūqā (d *c*912), Abū Bakr al-Rāzī, Avicenna, al-Šayzarī (fl *c*1190), Mūsā ibn ʿUbayd Allāh ibn Maymūn (Maimonides, d 1204) and al-Tīfāšī (Pormann 2007b). Another genre which proved to be surprisingly popular is that of the *Aphorisms*, short and pithy sayings that convey important insights in abbreviated form. The Hippocratic *Aphorisms* in their Arabic translation had a particularly strong impact; the first and most famous one was: 'Life is short, the art is long, the [right] time is fleeting, and experience dangerous' (Rosenthal 1966; Joosse, Pormann 2012). For instance, both al-Rāzī and Maimonides wrote books of medical aphorisms. Likewise, following Galen's example, physicians such as Avicenna's pupil ʿAbd al-Raḥmān ibn ʿAlī ibn abī Ṣādiq (d after 1068), Maimonides (d 1204), ʿAbd al-Laṭīf al-Baġdādī (d 1231), Ibn al-Quff (d 1286; see **no 28**), Ibn al-Nafīs (1288) and others all wrote commentaries on the Hippocratic *Aphorisms*. Such commentaries were not just derivative or scholastic, but could constitute venues for innovations and change, as the example of Ibn an-Nafīs' commentary on Avicenna's *Canon* demonstrates: it was there that he first described the pulmonary transit, as we have seen above. Like commentaries, the genre of the question-and-answer (*asʾila wa-ağwiba*) treatises was closely linked to medical teaching. Ḥunayn ibn Isḥāq wrote three such works: on medicine in general (*al-Masāʾil fī l-Ṭibb*), on ophthalmology (*al-Masāʾil fī l-ʿAyn*) and on the Hippocratic *Epidemics* (*Masāʾil al-Ibīḏīmīyā*) (Pormann 2008b). Other such works include the *Intelligent examination of all physicians* (*Imtiḥān al-alibbāʾ li-kāffat al-aṭibbāʾ*) by al-Sulamī (d c1208; ed Leiser and Khaledy 2003). The genre of the medical encyclopaedia in Arabic followed on from two trends of late antiquity: abridgment using *dihaíresis* (or division) to present the material in an easy fashion and the handbook, which provides a comprehensive overview of the topic. After the *Complete book of the medical art* (*Kāmil al-Ṣināʿa al-Ṭibbīya*) by al-Mağūsī (fl 983), Avicenna's *Canon of medicine* (*Kitāb al-Qānūn fī l-Ṭibb*) undoubtedly had the greatest impact on medicine in the Islamic and the Christian worlds. It was itself the subject of many abridgments, commentaries and supercommentaries (see chapter 2).

Medical practice

In the division of medicine into five parts, medical practice consists of prophylactics and therapeutics. For both these activities, diet or regimen (*tadbīr*) played a crucial role. Food obviously has a direct effect on one's well-being. The various foodstuffs were integrated into the system of humoral pathology and primary qualities. Some were seen to generate good humours such as blood, whereas others gave rise to diseases (Waines 1999). The control of body weight also played a significant role, and we find many recipes and instructions for a thinning diet (*tahzīl*). Exercise also served to preserve health. In this way, the physicians manipulated the 'six non-naturals' to prevent the patient from becoming ill or, if ill, to recover again.

Even for treatment of illnesses, diet was the first defence. Yet, we also find many important works on pharmacology. In this area, one has to distinguish between simple drugs (*adwiya mufrada*) and compound drugs (*adwiya murakkaba*). Simple drugs are single substances such as mint, honey, arsenic or opium, which possess certain qualities, both primary (dry, moist; hot, cold) and others (eg styptic, purging). Following Galen, these qualities were often rated in degrees from one (lowest) to four (and occasionally higher). Compound drugs consist of more than one ingredient, and could at times be very complicated. For instance, some recipes for theriac (*tiryāq*, from Greek *theriakḗ*) – a drug originally made to counter the effect of snake bites, and later used as a sort of panacea – contained dozens and dozens of different, and at times difficult to procure, ingredients. From a modern point of view, some ingredients seem highly effective (eg opium), whereas the usefulness of others is disputed (Tibi 2006; Chipman 2002).

Blood was removed both through venesection (or phlebotomy, *faṣd*; see **no 21**) and cupping (*ḥiğāma*; see **no 22**). In the former technique, one of the patient's veins was incised, and the blood would then run out. At times, blood was let in this way until the patient fainted. Two types of cupping existed: dry cupping and wet cupping. In both cases cupping glasses were applied to suck disease matter and superfluities out of the body. In the latter case, small incisions on the skin were also made, and some blood would come out of them. Physicians and surgeons also frequently resorted to cauterisation (*kayy*): a heated iron (or cautery, *mikwāh*) was put onto the skin so as to burn it; this would staunch bleeding and disinfect to some extent.

Bone-setting (*ğabr*) and surgery (*ğirāḥa*) also feature in the therapeutic arsenal described in the Arabic medical works. Sometimes extremely hazardous surgical procedures are explained in great detail, for instance that for umbilical hernias. It is, however, doubtful that these extremely hazardous surgical procedures were ever performed (Savage-Smith 2000). This raises the more general question as to what extent we can be confident that the therapeutic procedures described in the theoretical manuals were actually performed. Here, case notes are of paramount importance, and a number of them survive today. For instance, Abū Bakr al-Rāzī's students compiled a *Book of experiences* (*Kitāb al-Taǧārib*), which shows that in his daily practice he employed a much more limited range of drugs and treatments than those described in his other medical works (Álvarez-Millán 2000, 2010).

The sources offer little information about the patients' perspective, although in works of Arabic *belles lettres* there are a number of medical anecdotes. They report extraordinary cases, such as that of the Siamese twins, joined at the hip, who had to do everything together; of the girl near to death because of a tick in her vagina (its removal caused her great shame); and of one of al-Rāzī's patients who was accidentally cured when trying to commit suicide with snake poison out of sheer desperation over his painful condition (Bray 2006). In his *Revival of religious sciences* (*Iḥyāʾ ʿulūm al-dīn*), the philosopher and theologian al-Ġazālī (d 1111), relates the story of a physician telling an overweight woman that she is going to die in order to make her lose weight and be able to conceive. One can only speculate how she must have felt.

Medicine and society

Patients and practitioners operated within a wider societal context. For instance, one could become a physician in a number of ways. Some students learnt the medical art from their relatives, as the famous medical families of the Buḫtīšūʿs in the East and the Zuhrs in the West illustrate. Others learnt from experienced physicians to whom they served as apprentices. But we also find the case of a number of medical autodidacts, some of whom rose to great prominence, such as Ibn Riḍwān (d *c*1068) and Avicenna. The former reportedly was too poor to afford the expense of a medical teacher, and was therefore forced to study the art by himself (Leiser 1983). From the 10th century onwards, hospitals also became important venues for medical education (Pormann 2008c).

A prominent topic in recent scholarship is the Islamic hospital: what are its antecedents and in what way was it original? Certainly Byzantine institutions and notions of Christian charity, as well as late antique Greek medicine, played an important role (Horden 2008). Five factors, however, came together in Islamic hospitals which render them unique, and which together mark a significant departure from previous institutions. They are: legal and financial security through the status of pious foundation (*waqf*) in Islamic law; the 'secular' character of the medical therapy; the presence of elite practitioners; medical research; and medical teaching. The combination of these factors certainly constitutes innovation. Moreover, only the institutional setting made it possible for physicians like Abū Bakr Muḥammad al-Rāzī (d *c*925) to carry out large-scale research or to encounter rare diseases (Pormann 2008c, 2010c).

Elite physicians also endeavoured to distinguish themselves from other practitioners in the medical marketplace, with varying success. On the one hand, they argued for a canon of medical knowledge that all physicians should master in order to have access to the profession. For instance, in a manual on market inspection (*ḥisba*) from the 13th century, its author, the physician al-Šayzarī, demanded that physicians be tested according to the instructions given in Ḥunayn ibn Isḥāq's *On the examination of the physician* (*Fī Miḥnat al-ṭabīb*); ophthalmologists be examined on the content of Ḥunayn's *Ten treatises on the eye* (*al-ʿAšr maqālāt fī l-ʿayn*); bone setters on the sixth book of Paul of Aegina's medical encyclopaedia; and surgeons on Galen's *On the composition of simple drugs according to kinds*. Other manuals on medical ethics such as those by al-Ruhāwī (fl *c*850s) and Ṣāʿid ibn al-Ḥasan (d 1072), or on how to examine physicians, such as that by al-Sulamī, echo these injunctions. The canon of testable knowledge is largely based on Greek texts in Arabic translation. The famous physician and philosopher ʿAbd al-

Laṭīf al-Baġdādī even urged his readers to return to the example of Hippocrates and Galen (Joosse, Pormann 2010). In this way, the medical canon of textbooks serves as a touchstone. Yet, it is clear too from the same manuals on medical ethics and testing physicians that the medical elite rarely succeeded in excluding their competition. Al-Rāzī and Ṣāʿid ibn al-Ḥasan talk eloquently about their dismay that patients often turn to 'women and the rabble' instead of learned physicians like themselves (Pormann 2005).

Women in particular attracted the wrath of male physicians and yet much of the standard medical care, the 'bodywork', was probably carried out by them. Whether as mothers, sisters, aunts, grand-mothers, wise women, nurses or female physicians, women played a significant role in the medical marketplace. Yet, because the medical historiography was largely a male domain, and as the society as a whole was highly patriarchal, women's voices only reach us faintly across the centuries. Still, we have indirect evidence that women practised medicine in various guises. Women were not only practitioners, but also patients. Even if women would at times feel shame at being treated by male physicians, it appears that in extreme cases male doctors would even examine female genitalia. Such practices are justified by the Islamic legal principle of 'necessity' (*ḍarūra*): the woman's welfare outweighs other considerations. The famous 14th-century jurist Šams al-Dīn al-Ḏahabī (d *c*1348) touched on the question whether women can treat men and vice versa, and ruled that 'a man is allowed to treat a woman who is not his relation (*ağnabīya*), and to see her naked in the case of disease, just as a woman is allowed to treat a man and see him naked in the case of disease, when no man or close female family member (*maḥram*) is present [to treat him]' (Šams al-Dīn al-Ḏahabī 1996: 242).

Šams al-Dīn al-Ḏahabī made this statement in his manual on *Prophetic medicine* (*al-ṭibb al-nabawī*), also known as 'Medicine of the Prophet' (*ṭibb al-nabī*). This genre of medical (or rather, legal-medical) literature developed from the 10th century onwards. Legal scholars drew on collections of *ḥadīṯ* (utterances of the Prophet) and *sunna* (reports about the behaviour of the Prophet) to establish a religiously sound medical tradition. This genre gained greater prominence from the 13th century onwards. People sometimes think that the authors of the manuals on prophetic medicine wanted to counter the Greek influence. For the most part, nothing could be further from the truth, as many such manuals incorporated rather than rejected humoral pathology. The works by Šams al-Dīn al-Ḏahabī, as well as his contemporary Ibn Qayyim al-Ğawzīya (d 1350), include numerous references to the Greek authorities. In fact, after a preface that is religious in tone, the former begins with a concise explanation of human physiology according to Greek principles, saying:

> The constitution of Man is concerned with seven components. The first component is the elements which are four in number – fire which is hot and dry; air which is hot and wet; water which is cold and wet; and earth which is cold and dry. The second component is the mixtures that are nine in number. The first is an evenly balanced mixture. The second is an unevenly balanced mixture, which may be unmixed, being then hot, cold, moist, or dry. Etc.' (translation Elgood 1962: 49, slightly modified)

Therefore, we encounter here the four humours and four primary qualities. The literature on prophetic medicine therefore shows how profound the impact of humoral pathology was, affecting not only elite medical ideas, but also religious concepts (Perho 1995).

Religion and magic also played a role in other ways. When faced with illness, many Muslims, Christians and Jews reacted by praying to God and seeking His succour. But they went further: at times, they would, for instance, write certain *sūras* on a piece of paper and carry it as a pendant or drink water from bowls inscribed with Koranic

Fig 0.3 Portrait of Avicenna engraved by GP Busch.

verses. Here the line between licit religious practice and illicit use of magic (*siḥr*) is not always clear. In any case, we also have manuals on magic, spells and amulets, such as that attributed to the Egyptian scholar al-Būnī (d *c*1225) (Savage-Smith 2004); and we find magic spells next to pious incantations on medicinal bowls (see, for instance, **no 19**).

For the historiography of Islamic medicine, scholars have often relied disproportionately on Arabic bio-bibliographical works. These are works that provide biographies of scholars and physicians, together with lists of the books that they authored. They include titles such as the *Catalogue* (*Fihrist*) by Ibn al-Nadīm, a 10th-century Baghdad bookseller; the *Classes of physicians and learned men* (*Ṭabaqāt al-aṭibbāʾ wa-l-ḥukamāʾ*) by Ibn Ǧulǧul (d *c*994), a physician of Córdoba; the abridgment of Ibn al-Qifṭī's (d 1248) *History of learned men* (*Taʾrīkh al-ḥukamāʾ*) by al-Zawzanī (fl 1249); the *Essential information about the classes of physicians* (*ʿUyūn al-anbāʾ fī ṭabaqāt al-aṭibbāʾ*) by Ibn Abī Uṣaybiʿa (d 1270); and the *Discovery of opinions* (*Kašf al-ẓunūn*) by Ḥaǧǧī Ḫalīfa (Kātip Çelebī, d 1657). Over the past 30 years, scholars have increasingly tried to include more contemporaneous sources to write the history of Islamic medicine. There remains, however, a general perception of decline and fall after the age of Avicenna, which ought to be challenged vigorously (Joosse, Pormann 2010).

Medicine, in fact, continued to develop long after this allegedly classical age during the ʿAbbāsid heyday in different parts of the Ottoman Empire. Two examples can illustrate this. Dāwūd al-Anṭākī (d 1599), a physician from Syria, wrote the *Memorandum book for those who have understanding and collection of wondrous marvels* (*Taḏkirat ulī l-albāb wa-l-ǧāmiʿ li-l-ʿaǧab al-ʿuǧāb*). In it, he drew not only on the earlier Graeco-Arabic tradition exemplified by Avicenna's *Canon*, but also incorporated descriptions of new diseases such as syphilis, together with some European recipes. Likewise, the court physician Ṣāliḥ ibn Naṣr ibn Sallūm (d 1669) commissioned the translation of a treatise entitled *The new chemical medicine of Paracelsus* (*Kitāb al-Ṭibb al-ǧadīd al-kīmiyāʾī taʾlīf Barākalsūs*), in which a Christian colleague, called Nicolas, translated the work of two German followers of Paracelsus' chemical medicine (Bachour 2012; see **no 25**). Therefore the exchange of ideas between East and West did not stop at any particular time, nor was medicine stagnant. Even the many encounters with colonial medicine throughout the 19th century are not always one of Western superiority. For instance, in early 19th-century Egypt, the French physician A B Clot (1793–1868) shared many opinions with his Muslim colleagues (Anne-Marie Moulin, in Ebrahimnejad 2009, 42–58).

The impact of medieval Islamic medicine on Europe during the Middle Ages and the Renaissance can hardly be overestimated. In Italy, Spain and Antioch, many Arabic medical texts were translated into Latin. The two figures who excelled in these endeavours were Constantine the African (d before 1099), and Gerard of Cremona (d 1187). Not only did they translate the great encyclopaedias by Abū Bakr al-Rāzī (known in Latin as the *Book for al-Manṣūr* [*Liber ad Almansorem*]), al-Maǧūsī (*Royal book* [*Liber regius*]) and Avicenna (*Canon medicinae*; **no 8**), but also many monographs such as that by Isḥāq ibn ʿImrān (d *c* 904) *On melancholy* (*De melancholia*) or that by the Ibn al-Ǧazzār *On sexual intercourse* (*De coitu*). The *Introduction to medicine* (*al-Mudḫal fī l-Ṭibb*) by Ḥunayn ibn Isḥāq became known in Latin as *Isagoge Ioannitii*, and was core curriculum in most of the nascent European universities from the 13th century onwards. Likewise, during the European Renaissance, Avicenna's *Canon* was printed and reprinted dozens of times; it was also (together with the Koran) the first book to be printed in Europe in Arabic for the Arabic market (Siraisi 1987). Even the great Renaissance anatomist Andreas Vesalius (d 1564) wrote a paraphrase of al-Rāzī's *Book for al-Manṣūr* (**no 14**). There can therefore be no doubt that Arabic medicine in Latin translation had a profound and lasting impact on the history of medicine in the West. Some physicians during the Renaissance, however, resented the prominent position of Arabic medicine, and fought vigorously to erase the Arab and Muslim contribution to medicine (Pormann 2011c). At times, they succeeded in sidelining and removing the Arabic and Islamic heritage from the history books, although this trend is now declining.

Islamic medicine is also a continuous tradition. In many Muslim countries, the texts of Avicenna are eagerly read, and in souks one can buy the ingredients necessary to compose the various drugs. On the Indian sub-continent, this medical tradition has developed into what is nowadays called *Yūnānī Ṭibb* (lit 'Greek medicine'). Next to Ayurveda, it is the major classical medical tradition, and together with Muslim migrant communities has reached most corners of the world now. Likewise, the *Medicine of the Prophet* enjoys great popularity, and many of the works mentioned remain in print in numerous editions. Finally, there is also a large market for what one could call 'fusion medicine', syncretic collections of Greek humoral pathology and modern (Western) medicine that are commercially highly successful. Therefore, in many ways, the medical tradition that developed in the medieval Islamic world continues to thrive and grow in many different ways.

Further reading

For a study of the sources, the works by Ullmann (1970) and Sezgin (1970) remain fundamental. Good introductions include Ullmann (1978), Pormann, Savage-Smith (2007), Shefer Mossensohn (2009) and Pormann (2011a), all with further references. For a thorough assessment of medieval Arabo-Latin translations, see Burnett (2009).

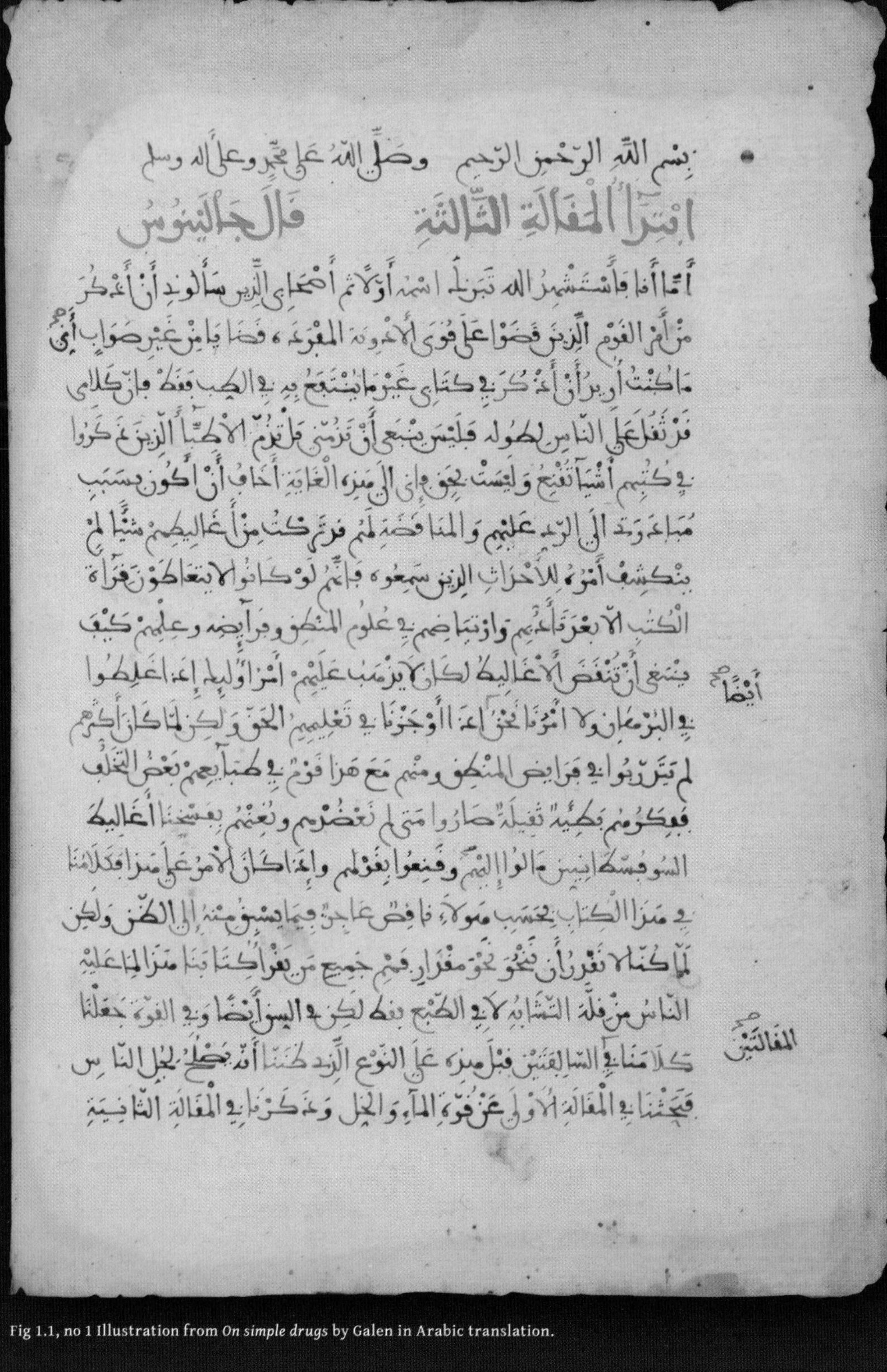
بسم الله الرحمن الرحيم وصلى الله على محمد وعلى آله وسلم

ابتدا المقالة الثالثة قال جالينوس

أما أنا فاستشهد الله تبارك اسمه أولا ثم أصحابي الذين سألوني أن أذكر
من أمر القوم الذين قضوا على قوى الأدوية المفردة قضايا من غير صواب أني
ما كنت أريد أن أذكر في كتابي غير ما ينتفع به في الطب فقط فإن كلامي
قد ثقل على الناس لطوله فليس ينبغي أن تذمني ولا تذم الأطبا الذين ذكروا
في كتبهم أشيا تقبح وليست تحق وإلى هذه الغاية أخاف أن أكون بسبب
مبادرتي إلى الرد عليهم والمناقضة لهم قد تركت من أغاليطهم شيئا لم
ينكشف أمره للأحداث الذين سمعوه فإنهم لو كانوا لا يتعاطون قراءة
الكتب إلا بعد أن يرتاضوا في علوم المنطق وفرايضه وعلموا كيف
ينبغي أن تنقض الأغاليط لكان لا يذهب عليهم أمرها ولما إذا غلطوا أيضا صح
في البرهان ولا أمرنا نحن إذا أوجزنا في تعليمهم الحق ولكن لما كان أكثرهم
لم يرتاضوا في فرايض المنطق ومنهم مع هذا قوم في طبايعهم بعض التخلف
فبعضهم بطيئة ثقيلة صاروا متى لم ننقض قولهم وننقض بفسخنا أغاليط
السوفسطائيين مالوا إليهم وقنعوا بقولهم وإذا كان الأمر على هذا فكلامنا
في هذا الكتاب بحسب هولاء ناقص عاجز فيما يشوقه إلى الظن ولكن
لما كنا لا نقدر أن نتحرى نحو مقدار فهم جميع من يقرأ كتابنا هذا ما عليه
الناس من قلة التشابه لا في الطبع فقط لكن في السن أيضا وفي القوة جعلنا
كلامنا في السابقتين قبل هذه على النوع الذي ظننا أنه يصلح لجل الناس المقالتين صح
فبحثنا في المقالة الأولى عن قوة الماء والخل وذكرنا في المقالة الثانية

Fig 1.1, no 1 Illustration from *On simple drugs* by Galen in Arabic translation.

Τῆς ἰατρικῆς τέχνης σκοπὸς μὲν ἡ ὑγίεια, τέλος δ' ἡ κτῆσις αὐτῆς. ἐξ ὧν δ' ἄν τις ἢ μὴ παροῦσαν ὑγίειαν ἐργάζοιτ' ἢ παροῦσαν διαφυλάττοι, γιγνώσκεσθαι μὲν ἀναγκαῖον τοῖς ἰατροῖς.

The aim of the art of medicine is health, but its end is the possession of health. Doctors have to know by which means to bring about health, when it is absent, and by which means to preserve it, when it is present. (Galen of Pergamum (tr Frede 1985: 3))

1 In the beginning there was Galen

Galen of Pergamum (*c*129–216) emerged as the central figure in medicine not only in the Greek, but also in the Latin, Syriac and Arabic traditions. His main contribution to medicine was threefold.

First, he refashioned Hippocrates in his own image by commenting on those writings attributed to Hippocrates with which he agreed. For instance, he wrote long commentaries on the *Aphorisms* (a collection of medical sayings) and *Prognostics* (a treatise on how to recognise diseases and predict their future course), but regarded *On ancient medicine* as spurious, because it rejected the idea of a medical theory such as humoral pathology. This theory, first set out in the Hippocratic treatise *On the nature of man*, maintains that health consists of the balance of the four humours: black bile, yellow bile, blood and phlegm. Galen also wrote a commentary on *On the nature of man*, and thus lent authority to this theory, which was to rule medicine for the next millennium and a half.

Second, he greatly advanced medicine in a number of areas. For instance, his anatomical experimentations on live animals not only constituted great spectacles for the Roman population, but also advanced the understanding of the workings of the body. He quite considerably expanded the therapeutic arsenal at the disposal of the physician. For instance, his works on simple and compound drugs are milestones in the evolution of pharmacology; and his massive work *On the method of healing* offered fresh insights into how to deal with various conditions; it was translated into Latin by Thomas Linacre (1460–1524). He also wrote profusely on questions of medical epistemology in an effort to formulate rules to find and assess new treatments. His short treatise *On the sects for beginners* remained the first introduction for generations of medical students in East and West, and its first sentence also opens (in slightly modified form) the famous *Canon of medicine* (see below p21).

Third, Galen succeeded in canonising himself. He wrote a vast medical œuvre; we know of more than 440 titles, although not all works have survived, and some may well have been falsely attributed to Galen. This said, he was extremely prolific. Towards the end of his life, Galen wrote not only an annotated list of all his works, but also gave instructions as to how to read them. He offered an all-encompassing account of medicine that subsequent generations continued to read and study. In this way, Galen gave rise to Galenism. And this Galenism served as the foundation for both the later Arabic and Latin medical tradition.

Galen is therefore the most important medical writer of antiquity, and perhaps the most influential one of all times. He and other medical writers such as Dioscorides of Anazarbus (fl 1st century), Rufus of Ephesus (fl *c*100) and Paul of Aegina (fl 650s) were all translated into Arabic in the course of the 9th century. These translations of medical texts formed part of a larger Graeco-Arabic translation movement that Dimitri Gutas (1998: 8) has rightly compared in terms of scope and historical importance to Pericles' Athens and Renaissance Italy. Gutas argued that the impulse behind the translation movement should not be seen as monocausal: it was not just one factor that led to most Greek philosophical, medical and scientific texts available in late antiquity being translated into Arabic. The economic situation certainly played a role: when the ʿAbbāsid dynasty came to power in the 750s, they achieved prosperity at the crossroads of different trade routes and the agriculturally productive lands of the Fertile Crescent. Their ideology also had an impact. Their outlook was more cosmopolitan than that of the Umayyads (who ruled *c*660–750): the ʿAbbasids deliberately adopted Sassanian court rituals to appeal to their Persian supporters and clients; and they promoted the idea that Greek thought actually goes back to old Persian sources that had been translated into Greek after Alexander's conquests and deposited in the famous Alexandrian library. Moreover, by moving their capital further east through the foundation of Baghdad, they benefitted from an extremely multilingual environment in which oral and written translations had a long history. Finally, although many of the translators were Syriac-speaking Christians, it is wrong to see the translation movement as a Christian affair. The sponsors belonging to the ʿAbbasid elite financed and facilitated the translation movement; without their support, it would hardly have achieved the same scale.

Whereas Gutas stressed the multifaceted nature of the translation movement, George Saliba (2007) argued that the translation movement had its roots in the administrative reforms brought about by the caliph ʿAbd al-Malik in the late 7th century; he Arabised the administration (*dīwān*), thus replacing Greek and Persian as administrative languages in the western and eastern parts of the Umayyad empire, respectively. This, Saliba maintained, led to unemployment of Greek- and Syriac-speaking Christians, who then turned to the sciences in an effort to regain their lost monopoly on knowledge. Therefore, according to Saliba, the translation movement started earlier, in the early rather than the late eighth century; and the motivation was not so much the patronage of the ʿAbbāsid elite, but the reforms of an Umayyad caliph.

Saliba's account of the translation movement (his 'alternative narrative', as he called it) does not, however, do justice to this complex phenomenon (Pormann 2010b). Gutas is right in arguing that the Graeco-Arabic translation movement resulted from favourable economic conditions, a cosmopolitan outlook that deliberately embraced other cultures, and a genuinely polyglot environment. Here the recourse to a Greek past was particularly important as the scientific and medical tradition largely went beyond country and creed. To be sure, most Greek doctors and scientists adhered to the polytheism prevalent in the classical world, but their religious beliefs played a very minor role in the theory and practice of science and medicine (Strohmaier 2012). Christians, Jews, Muslims and pagans could all equally adopt humoral pathology, as it did not threaten any of their belief systems. Another idea about the translation movement, put forward for instance by Bernhard Lewis (2002: 139), has some currency: namely, that Muslims were interested only in what they perceived as useful (philosophy being seen as a useful subject). And to be sure, very little Greek poetry has been translated into Arabic. There was, however, significant interest in Greek literature more generally. Popular collections of pithy sayings (*gnomologia*) became available in Arabic and were eagerly read (Overwien 2005). They even included some Greek verse and the *Alexander romance* had a tremendous impact in Arabic (Doufikar-Aerts 2010).

Therefore, although the criterion of usefulness cannot be excluded as a contributing factor to why Greek medical texts were translated into Arabic, it was certainly not the only one. Nor does Saliba's vision of the translation movement apply to medical texts, as Manfred Ullmann's recent work amply demonstrates. Ullmann (2002, 2006, 2007, 2009, 2011–12) has shown how translators of medical (and also philosophical) texts acquired greater sophistication and accuracy over the course of the 9th century: whereas the translator al-Biṭrīq in the second half of the 8th century still often resorted to paraphrase and transliteration, Ḥunayn ibn Isḥāq and those in his translation workshop achieved greater precision, but were also able to draw on a more established Arabised technical vocabulary.

We are particularly well informed about how Galen was rendered into Arabic, as Ḥunayn ibn Isḥāq wrote an *Epistle* (*Risāla*) on how he and his team translated the various Galenic works. On numerous occasions Ḥunayn tells us about his efforts to locate Greek or Syriac manuscripts, so as to produce a better text. His translations are therefore philological achievements in their own right. Like Galen before him, Ḥunayn tried to reconstruct the medical ideas of his source, even where the Greek text is corrupt (Vagelpohl 2011). And when Ḥunayn translated Galenic commentaries on Hippocratic works and had to interpret the often difficult Ionic prose of the Hippocratic text, he followed Galen in his interpretations (Overwien 2012). Therefore, Ḥunayn is heavily influenced by Galen in the way that he read, understood and explained the Hippocratic texts. Likewise, during the European Renaissance, we see that John Caius (1510–73) collected different Galenic manuscripts in order to edit Galen's works and to translate them into Latin. Both Ḥunayn and Caius followed in Galen's philological footsteps to bring his works to their contemporaries.

Fig 1.2 Portrait of John Caius (1510–73) by Claude Speechley, 1882.

Further reading

Nutton's (2013) updated second edition of his *Ancient medicine* provides an authoritative and well documented introduction to the subject with further references. Gutas' (1998) account of the translation movement is still unsurpassed, although Saliba (2007) offers an alternative interpretation (although unpersuasive to my mind; see Pormann 2010b). Pormann (2004a) provides a detailed and quite technical study on how one author, Paul of Aegina, was transmitted into Syriac and Arabic. For recent work on the role of Syriac in the Graeco-Arabic translation process, see Bhayro *et al* (2013), with further references.

Exhibition items

› No 1 (MSTR22): Galen's *On simple drugs* in Arabic translation

The second and third books of Galen's treatise *On simple drugs*, translated into Arabic in Ḥunayn ibn Isḥāq's workshop.

This unbound manuscript is written in Maġribī script and therefore comes from the West of the Arabic-speaking world; it possibly dates back to the 14th or 15th century. The manuscript contains part of Galen's *On simple drugs* in the Arabic translation. Galen's work *On simple drugs* consists of 11 books, the first five dealing with the theory of simple drugs, and the last six containing an alphabetical list of simple drugs. In the latter part, Galen would normally describe the appearance and properties of the drug in question. For a further discussion of pharmacology, see chapter 6 below.

Galen's *On simple drugs* is of incredible importance for the study of how Greek texts were rendered into Syriac and Arabic, since it is the only Galenic text for which we can compare an older and a newer Syriac translation, and an older and a newer Arabic translation. In other words, we can trace here the development of translation techniques from the 6th to the 9th centuries (Pormann 2012b). The older Syriac translation is that by Sergius of Rēš ʿAynā (d 536). It survives only partially: a British Library manuscript preserves books 6–8; and a privately owned palimpsest preserves at least books 6–9, but possibly the whole second half, books 6–11 (Bhayro *et al* 2012, 2013). Ḥunayn often criticised Sergius' Syriac translations as inadequate or faulty in his *Epistle*. Yet only recently has it become possible to compare Ḥunayn's Syriac translation with that of Sergius. For most of Ḥunayn's Syriac translations are lost today. But we can recover Ḥunayn's rendering of Galen's *On simple drugs* from quotations contained in Ḥunayn's own work *On the properties of foodstuffs*.

A recent study came to the conclusion that Ḥunayn's Syriac rendering does display greater sophistication and a deeper understanding of the finer nuances of the Greek source text, but that it also depends to a much greater extent on Sergius' translation than previously thought (Bhayro *et al* 2013: 139–43). In other words, Ḥunayn did not really do justice to his predecessor Sergius when lambasting the latter for his perceived faults.

Let us now turn to the two Arabic translations of *On simple drugs*. Manfred Ullmann (2002) showed that an Istanbul manuscript contained an earlier translation by someone called al-Biṭrīq for book 6, and he subsequently compared this older rendering from the late 8th century with that produced in Ḥunayn's workshop (which is also the one contained in the RCP manuscript displayed here). Ullmann concluded that the older translator did not have the same intimate grasp of Greek that Ḥunayn possessed. For instance, where Ḥunayn would render the same Greek term through various Arabic ones to bring out the different nuances, al-Biṭrīq simply used the same Arabic term. Moreover, whereas Ḥunayn went to great length to mirror the complex Greek sentences with their subordinate clauses, al-Biṭrīq employed coordination (or parataxis) in an effort to simplify his prose.

This manuscript thus exemplifies the efforts of the 9th-century translators, who made available in Arabic most Greek medical texts. But is also illustrates the multifaceted nature of this translation movement and its long history, in which Syriac translations often played an important role. The exact nature of this role has only recently come under scholarly scrutiny, and much remains to be discovered in this area.

> No 2 (Fc.2.06): *Eton Galen*: John Caius' copy of Galen's *Collected works* in Greek

This is the second complete edition of Galen's extant works in Greek, published in Basle by Cratander in 1538.

This particular copy was owned by John Caius (1510–73), a fellow and president of the RCP, and is now known as the 'Eton Galen' (Nutton 1987). Through it, one can tell the story of the English medical humanism, in which the RCP played such an important role. To give some background: the first edition of the *Complete works of Galen* appeared in Venice in 1525 and was published by the Aldine Press. Thirteen years later, a consortium of Basle printers, led by Cratander, published what one might call a second edition. This edition claims to be 'corrected and restored according to many ancient manuscripts, as if born again'. One of those engaged in this Basle edition was the German physician Leonhard Fuchs (1501–66) – best known now for having given his name to the fuchsia. He was a fierce advocate for a return to the Greek sources, but also opposed all Arabic influences in medicine, which he described as nefarious (Pormann 2011c).

Be that as it may, both Thomas Linacre (1460–1524), the first president of the RCP, and John Caius had a strong interest in Galen, and translated several works of his into Latin. Caius in particular was animated by a great zeal to find additional Greek copies of Galen, and he edited a significant number of Galenic texts, some for the first time. Throughout his life, Caius recorded variant readings that he encountered in the many manuscripts he saw in the margins of his 1538 copy of the *Complete works of Galen*. These annotations are of incredible value, even today, as they appear to reflect the readings of certain manuscripts that are lost to us now. Another fellow of the Royal College, Theodore Goulston (*c*1575–1632), recognised the importance of Caius' annotations and used them in his own philological work on Galen. Goulston had transferred from

Fig 1.3 Opening page of the Eton Galen, Γαληνοῦ ἅπαντα, 1538 © Eton College.

Peterhouse, Cambridge, to Merton College, Oxford in 1595, and become a fellow of Merton in 1596, where he later occupied the Linacre fellowship. We know that Eton College bought Caius' copy in 1600–01. Here the Merton connection appears important, as Sir Henry Savile (1549–1622), the provost of Eton, was also the warden of Merton College; Savile took an interest in both classical learning and mathematics. Eton's records show that the copy was bought from a 'Dr James', and Nutton has suggested that this may have been Dr John James (*c*1550–1601), who was censor of the RCP on three occasions

This Eton Galen illustrates the Ovidian saying that 'books have their fate' (*habent sua fata libelli*): medical humanism led to a quest for manuscripts and variant readings. But this medical humanism was not innocent or value-free, as the example of Leonard Fuchs shows. Fuchs inveighed repeatedly against Arab physicians, claiming that 'the Arabs spread nothing but obscurity' and concluding that 'it is best to sideline and simply reject the Arab authors' (Pormann 2011c: 296, 298). Although Fuchs was the most severe and vociferous critic of Arabic medicine, other humanist authors engaged in editing Galen displayed a similar attitude; and they included such luminaries as Symphorien Champier (1472–1538 or 1539), Niccolò Leoniceno (1428–1524) and Giovanni Manardi (1462–1536). The massive Arabic contribution to the history of medicine was slowly forgotten from the 17th to the 20th centuries, in part, undoubtedly, because of humanist attitudes. This forgotten heritage deserves to be highlighted and studied, and the present exhibition – and this catalogue – hopes to make a contribution to its rediscovery.

Finally, one should stress that although Ḥunayn ibn Isḥāq, the great 9th-century translator, and John Caius were separated by centuries and hundreds of miles, both endeavoured to recover Galen through an arduous search for manuscripts, and to make him available to their contemporaries by translating the newly recovered works, be it into Syriac and Arabic, or into Latin.

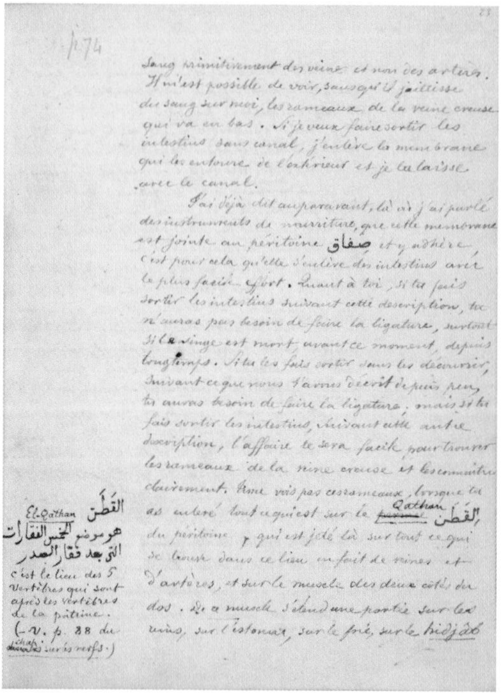
p. 74

Sang uniquement des veines et non des artères. Il m'est possible de voir, sans qu'il jaillisse du sang sur moi, les rameaux de la veine creuse qui va en bas. Si je veux faire sortir les intestins sans canal, j'enlève la membrane qui les entoure de l'extérieur et je la laisse avec le canal.

J'ai déjà dit auparavant, là où j'ai parlé des instruments de nourriture, que cette membrane est jointe au péritoine صفاق et y adhère. C'est pour cela qu'elle s'enlève des intestins avec le plus facile effort. Quant à toi, si tu fais sortir les intestins suivant cette description, tu n'auras pas besoin de faire la ligature, surtout si le singe est mort avant ce moment, depuis longtemps. Si tu les fais sortir sans les découvrir, suivant ce que nous t'avons décrit depuis peu, tu auras besoin de faire la ligature; mais si tu fais sortir les intestins suivant cette autre description, l'affaire te sera facile pour trouver les rameaux de la veine creuse et les connaître clairement. Tu ne vois pas ces rameaux, lorsque tu as enlevé tout ce qui est sur le Qathan القطن, du péritoine, qui est jeté là sur tout ce qui se trouve dans ce lieu en fait de veines et d'artères, et sur le muscle des deux côtés du dos. De ce muscle s'étend une partie sur les reins, sur l'estomac, sur le foie, sur le hidjâb

El-Qathan القَطَن
هو موضع الخمس الفقارات التي بعد فقار الصدر
c'est le lieu des 5 vertèbres qui sont après les vertèbres de la poitrine.
(– v. p. 88 du chap. sur les nerfs.)

Fig 1.4, no 3 French translation of Arabic manuscript of Galen's *De anatomicis administrationibus*, 1854.

> **No 3** (MS269/5): modern manuscript of Gustave Dugat's French translation made on the basis of an Arabic version of Galen's *Anatomical procedures*

> **No 4** (copy no 3358-9, SL 611(02)"a"): First printed Arabic version and German translation of Galen's *Anatomical procedures*, books 9 to 15

These two items illustrate the passion with which physicians and philologists during the 19th century tried to use an Arabic translation of an otherwise lost Greek text, namely books 9 to 15 of Galen's *Anatomical procedures*. It is a fascinating story of unrealised academic ambitions, but also of national rivalry. To understand what happened, it is necessary to give some background.

Galen's *Anatomical procedures* is a work in which he explains how to dissect animals in order to reveal their anatomy; it also contains descriptions of animal vivisections that Galen performed in Rome in front of an audience. Galen inferred from animal anatomy to human anatomy, and that led to numerous problems. Vesalius, for instance, criticised Galen repeatedly for confusing animal with human anatomy in his *On the fabric of the human body* (see **no 14**). Be that as it may, Galen's work comprised 15 books, but only the first 8 and part of book 9 survive in Greek; the rest (the latter part of book 9 and books 10 to 15) are lost. But in the 9th century, when Ḥunayn ibn Isḥāq and his colleagues were engaged in translating this text into Arabic, they still had access to all 15 books in Greek. It was therefore possible to read and study the lost books in Arabic translation. Already in the 1620s, the Dutch orientalist Jacob Golius (d 1667) obtained a complete copy of this Arabic translation, probably in Syria. Golius appears to have realised the importance of manuscript for recovering the lost Galen, for he had Nicolaus

Petraeus make a copy of books 10 to 15. Narcissus Marsh (1638–1713), Archbishop of Armagh, purchased part of Golius' private collection of manuscripts in 1696, and Marsh's Arabic manuscripts came into the Bodleian library after his death in 1713; the medieval exemplar bears the shelfmark MS Marsh 158, whereas Petraeus' Renaissance copy bears that of MS Marsh 448 (Savage-Smith 2011; **no 17**).

In the intervening years, these two manuscripts remained in relative obscurity, until William A Greenhill announced in 1844 in the *London Medical Gazette* that the lost seven books of Galen's *Anatomical procedures* had been rediscovered through the Bodleian manuscripts (Gourevitch 1997). At the time, Greenhill was 30 years of age, and until his death half a century later, he was animated by a desire to publish this Arabic translation and translate it, or have it translated, so as to recover the Greek original. To this end, he entered into correspondence with Charles Daremberg already in January 1845; Daremberg (1817–72) had written a doctoral thesis on Galen's anatomy in 1841, and was a rising star in French medical circles. Daremberg had not learned much if any Arabic by then, and although he later had the most famous French orientalist, Ernest Renan, for a teacher, he never progressed much in Arabic. The RCP possesses part of a long correspondence between Greenhill and Daremberg from 1845 until Daremberg's death, which tells the story of how Greenhill endeavoured to join forces with Daremberg to edit, first, all of Galen, and then, more modestly, the lost seven books of the *Anatomical procedures*. In this correspondence, the two disagree, for instance, about the language into which Galen should be translated. Daremberg favoured the vernacular, that is, French, whereas Greenhill had no doubt that the translation should be in Latin, as he explains: 'I am very sorry to hear of the proposed change in the plan ... with respect to the French translation ... I should equally object to an English or German translation joined to the text which (if the work is intended for scholars all over Europe and not merely for Frenchmen) should have a Latin version annexed to it' (Letter to Daremberg of 17 March 1848; quoted according to Gourevitch 1997: 434). But Greenhill made very little progress towards editing the Arabic translation, and Daremberg got more and more anxious to have access to it. For this reason, he secured the collaboration of a compatriot, Gustave Dugat (1824–94), a French orientalist at the beginning of his career in the early 1850s when Daremberg approached him. Dugat must have made a copy of the Oxford manuscripts by 1854, and probably translated book 9 in the period shortly thereafter. This manuscript translation is item **no 3**. But it was a fairly hasty affair, and in need of revision, as the author himself freely acknowledged. It was to serve as an initial draft, giving Daremberg a very provisional first impression about the content, but Dugat never revised it. After Daremberg's death, Greenhill urged Dugat to return to this work, but after years of dithering and provarication, the latter finally announced in 1882 that he would be unable to find the time to do so. Greenhill then received an inquiry from an American correspondent who showed an interest in pursuing the project to edit and translate the Arabic version of the lost books, and Greenhill's daughter pursued the correspondence after her father's death in 1895. But all these endeavours remained largely fruitless. Only the various correspondences between Greenhill, Daremberg and Dugat, as well as some of their papers and working notes, attest to their desire to produce a critical edition and scholarly translation.

It was only in 1905 and without any direct relationship to efforts discussed above that the German physician and Arabist Max Simon published the lost *Seven books of Galen's anatomy* (*Sieben Bücher Anatomie des Galen*).

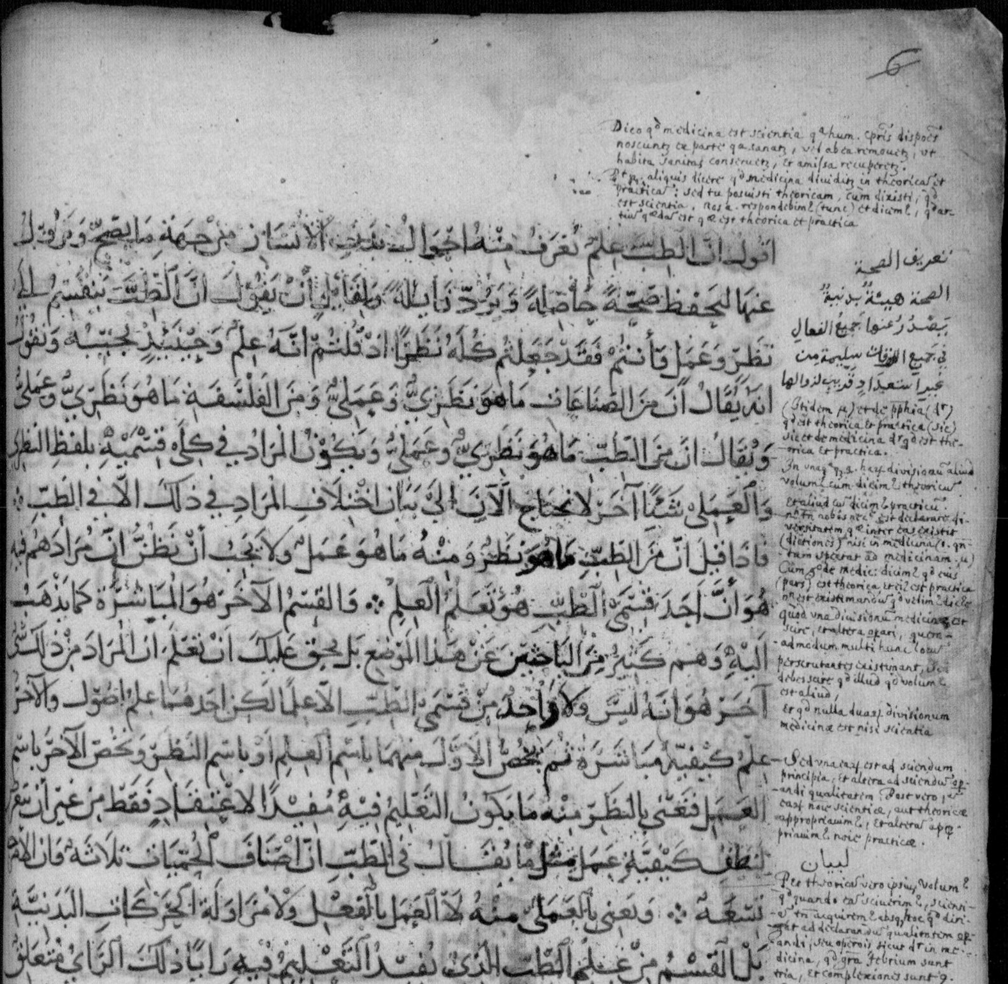

Dico q^d medicina est scientia q^a hum. cpris dispoes noscuntr ex parte q^a sanatr, vel ab ea removetr, ut habita sanitas conservetr, et amissa recuperetr.

Et ps. aliquis dicere q^d medicina dividitr in theoricam et practicam: sed tu posuisti theoricam, cum dixisti, q^d est scientia. Res. respondebimr (tunc) et dicimr, q^d artium q^e dam est q^e est theorica et practica

أقول إن الطب علم يتعرف منه أحوال بدن الإنسان من جهة ما يصح ويزول
عنها ليحفظ صحة حاصلة ويستردها زائلة ولقائل أن يقول إن الطب ينقسم إلى
نظر وعمل وأنتم فقد جعلتم كله نظريا إذ قلتم إنه علم وحينئذ نجيبه ونقول
إنه يقال إن من الصناعات ما هو نظري وعملي ومن الفلسفة ما هو نظري وعملي
ويقال إن من الطب ما هو نظري وعملي ويكون المراد في كل قسمة بلفظ النظري
والعملي شيئا آخر ولا نحتاج الآن إلى بيان اختلاف المراد في ذلك إلا في الطب
فإذا قيل إن من الطب ما هو نظري ومنه ما هو عمل ولا يجب أن يظن أن مرادهم فيه
هو أن أحد قسمي الطب هو تعلم العلم والقسم الآخر هو المباشرة كما يذهب
إليه وهم كثير من الباحثين عن هذا الموضع بل يحق عليك أن تعلم أن المراد من ذلك
آخر هو أنه ليس ولا واحد من قسمي الطب إلا علما لكن أحدهما علم أصول والآخر
علم كيفية مباشرة ثم يخص الأول منهما باسم العلم أو باسم النظر ويخص الآخر باسم
العمل فنعني بالنظر منه ما يكون التعليم فيه مفيد الاعتقاد فقط من غير أن يتعرض
لبيان كيفية عمل مثل ما يقال في الطب إن أصناف الحميات ثلاثة وإن الأمزجة
تسعة ونعني بالعملي منه لا العمل بالفعل ولا مزاولة الحركات البدنية
بل القسم من علم الطب الذي يفيد التعليم فيه رأيا وذلك الرأي متعلق
بكيفية عمل مثل ما يقال في الطب إن الأورام الحارة يجب أن يقرب إليها في
الابتداء ما يردع ويبرد ويكثف ثم من بعد ذلك تمزج الرادعات بالمرخيات
ثم بعد الانتهاء إلى الانحطاط يقتصر على المرخيات المحللة إلا في أورام عن مواد
تدفعها الأعضاء الرئيسة فهذا العلم يفيد لك رأيا هو بيان كيفية عمل فإذا علمت
هذين القسمين فقد حصل لك علم علمي وعلم عملي وإن لم تعمل قط ولا تعالج
أيضا نقول إن أحوال بدن الإنسان ثلاثة الصحة والمرض

تعريف الصحة
الصحة هيئة بدنية
يصدر عنها جميع الأفعال
في جميع الأوقات سليمة من
غير استعداد قريب لزوالها

(Ibidem μ) et de φphia (Γ) q^d est theorica et practica (sic) dicit de medicina q^d est theorica et practica.

In unaq. q. haec divisionum aliud volumr cum dicimr theoricum et aliud cum dicimr practicum. Non tn nobis nec^e est declarare diversitatem q^e inter eas existit (dictiones) nisi in medicina (i. quantum spectat ad medicinam.) Cum q^d de medic. dicimr q^d eius (pars) est theorica et alia est practica non est existimandum q^d velimr dicere quod una divisionum medicinae est scire, et altera operari, quemadmodum multi hunc locum perscrutantes existimant. Sed debes scire q^d illud q^d volumr est aliud, et q^d nulla duarum divisionum medicinae est nisi scientia

Sed una earum est ad sciendum principia, et altera ad sciendum operandi qualitatem. Post vero, earum unam scientiae, aut theoricae appropriamr, et alteram appropriamr nomine practicae.

بيان

Per theoricam vero ipsius volumr q^d quando eas scierimr, scientiam tn acquirimr ... q^d dirigat ad declarandum qualitatem operandi, sicut d^r in medicina, q^d gn^a febrium sunt tria, et complexiones sunt 9.

Et per practicam ipsius volumr non operacm in effu, neq. laborem motionum cprearum, sed divisionem scientiae medic. q^e cum eas scierimr auxiliabitr nobis ad inquirendam scientiam vel opinionem a q^a dependet modus operandi.

Sicut d^r in medicina, q^d apostematibus calidis adhibenda sunt in principio q^e repellant, et infrigident et inspissent, et postea repellentia cum mollificantibus permiscebimr, deinde post statum in declinat. mollificantibus resolutivis, nisi (i. exceptis) apostematibus, q^a ... ex meritis, quas membra expellunt principalia.

علم علمي

Haec g^r doctrina in sntia auxiliatr (i. consilium suppeditat μ) et haec sntia est declaratio qualitatis (sive modi) operandi. Cumq. duarum divisionum qualitatem scieris, iam scientiam scientialem, et scientiam operativam adeptus eris, etsi nunquam operatus fueris

Fig 2.1, no 5 Definition of medicine from book one of Avicenna's *Canon*, 1214.

الطب علم تعرف منه أحوال بدن الإنسان من جهة ما يصح
ويزول عن الصحة ليحفظ الصحة حاصلة وتستردها زائلة.

Medicine is the science through which one knows the states of the human body insofar as they are healthy or unhealthy, in order to preserve health when it is present, and to restore it when it is absent. (Avicenna, *Canon of medicine*)

2 Avicenna and his legacy

Avicenna (Ibn Sīnā, d 1037) is undoubtedly the towering figure in Arabo-Islamic medicine. No other author had such an impact on generations of physicians in both East and West. But Avicenna also stirred up controversy among medical historians, and therefore makes for an extremely interesting subject. His major work is the *Canon of medicine* (*al-Qānūn fī l-ṭibb*), a medical encyclopaedia in five books. Book one, also called 'Generalities' (*Kullīyāt*), gives an outline of the fundamental principles of medicine, including physiology and anatomy. Books two and five deal with simple and compound drugs, respectively, and books three and four list diseases, the former diseases that are specific to a certain part or place of the body, arranged from tip to toe, and the latter other diseases.

The opening quotation in this section illustrates that Avicenna owed a great debt to previous medical authors, and notably Galen. For Avicenna's definition of medicine resembles that given by Galen at the beginning of his *On the sects for beginners* (see above, p13). In fact, Avicenna continued two trends of late antique medical writing in his *Canon of medicine*. It follows in the tradition of medical encyclopaedias written by Oribasius, Aëtius of Amida, Alexander of Tralles and Paul of Aegina. Paul of Aegina in particular was a constant source of inspiration, not only on the level of content, but also as a model of how to draft a tightly organised medical handbook (Pormann 2004a). Al-Rāzī and al-Mağūsī also wrote encyclopaedias – the *Book for al-Manṣūr* (*al-Kitāb al-Manṣūrī*; see **no 14**) and the *Complete book on the medical art* (*Kāmil al-ṣināʿa al-ṭibbīya*), respectively – thus continuing the Greek genre. The latter in particular had a significant influence on Avicenna. The second trend from late antiquity visible in the *Canon of medicine* is the organisation of knowledge through division (or *dihaíresis* in Greek). We have seen in the introduction that division played a significant part in the medical education in late antique Alexandria, as it is reflected in the commentaries, summaries and branch diagrams that have come down to us (Pormann 2010a).

But if Avicenna's *Canon* draws so heavily on late antique models both in form and in content, what then is its contribution to the development of medicine? Was Avicenna merely a skilled scholastic author, able to summarise and organise previous medical knowledge, or did he innovate in medicine, as he did in philosophy? This leads us to a recent debate about Avicenna's clinical practice. Cristina Álvarez-Millán (2010) argued that Avicenna's reputation as a clinician owes more to myth than historical fact. Although Avicenna mentions clinical practice in his autobiography, and later sources such as the *Four discourses* (*Čahār maqāla*) by the 12th-century Persian prose author Samarqandī record certain clinical cases, Álvarez-Millán insists that they represent literary motifs rather than reality. In conclusion, Álvarez-Millán (2010: 209) states that the *Canon* 'not only made available an extensive systematization of medical knowledge, but also synthesized the dispersed and fragmentary medical literature existing at the time, mainly Galenic treatises blended with Aristotelian natural philosophy'.

Yet Álvarez-Millán is wrong in denying that Avicenna practised medicine and she exaggerates when characterising the *Canon* merely as a systematisation of previous Galenic and Aristotelian knowledge (Pormann 2013a). Let us look at Avicenna's medical practice first. It is true that he valued theoretical sciences much more highly than practical ones, being a true Aristotelian in this sense. Even in the opening chapter of his *Canon of medicine*, he makes the point that he is concerned with the theory of medicine here, as well as the theory of medical practice, but not with actual practice (*mubāšara*) (Gutas 2003; reprinted 2011: 36–7). But even though the *Canon of medicine* is therefore largely a theoretical book, it is not devoid of new insights. In dozens of places, for instance, Avicenna remarks that he 'experienced' or 'tested' (*ǧarraba*) certain treatments and drugs himself. For instance, Álvarez-Millán has doubted the account of Avicenna's treating a patient suffering from love-sickness (*ʿišq*), because the method by which he diagnosed the disease – feeling the pulse and mentioning names and locations connected with the beloved – had already been described by Galen and had become topical. Yet in the chapter on love-sickness in the *Canon*, Avicenna insists repeatedly that he treated patients in this way (Pormann 2013a: 97). Therefore, it is clear that Avicenna must have had at least some practical experience as a physician, and this is reflected even in a mostly theoretical book, the *Canon of medicine*.

But it is also unfair to describe Avicenna's contribution in the *Canon* mostly as a compilation from earlier Greek sources for another reason. Avicenna is rightly regarded as one of the most innovative philosophical thinkers (Adamson 2013). Therefore, it would be quite surprising, if he merely compiled information in his *Canon of medicine*. That he went well beyond Aristotle and Galen can be shown with the example of the inner senses. Avicenna introduced the concept of the inner senses, and notably that of estimation (Arabic *wahm*, Latin *aestimatio*). It is a mental faculty situated in the middle ventricle of the brain, and lies conceptually between imagination and thinking. For instance, a sheep might know instinctively that it should flee from the wolf. Sheep obviously do not have the gift of rational thought, but their aversion to wolves goes beyond mere perception or imagination. Avicenna discusses estimation both in his *Canon of medicine* and in his *Cure*, a philosophical encyclopaedia. (See Pormann 2013a: 102–7 for a fuller discussion.) This example shows that Avicenna integrates a new philosophical concept into his medical work, and is not content merely to repeat (or summarise) previous knowledge.

The celebrated translator Gerard of Cremona (d 1187) rendered the *Canon of medicine* from Arabic into Latin (for more information about Gerard, see **no 15**). It is hard to overestimate the influence of the *Canon of medicine* (or *Canon medicinae*) in Latin. Already in the Middle Ages, numerous copies were produced, and various physicians began to write their own commentaries on the *Canon*. Let us just mention the two most influential ones: Gentile da Foligno (d 1348) and Jacques Despars (d 1458). The former came from Bologna, but spent most of his professional life in Perugia, where he also died. It is there that he wrote his massive commentary on all five books of the *Canon*, probably during the last 30 years of his life. Despars hardly worked more quickly, writing his commentary over the period of some 20 years. This commentary activity illustrates that the *Canon* had become canonical: it was often used, in excerpts to be sure, for teaching medicine, and as a medical reference work. With the invention of the printing press, the *Canon medicinae* reached new audiences by being printed and reprinted repeatedly, either on its own or together with the commentaries of Gentile de Foligno and others. It continued to be dominant in most European universities until the 17th century. No fewer than 60 editions of the Latin text (in whole or in part) were printed in the 16th and 17th century (Siraisi 1987). And in Italy in particular, it was still used in the 18th century as well.

The *Canon*'s fate in the Arabic- and Persian-speaking East was hardly less impressive. For instance, the Jewish physician Ibn Ǧumayᶜ (d 1198), the Muslim philosopher and thinker Faḫr al-Dīn al-Rāzī (d 1210), the Muslim physician and jurisconsult Ibn al-Nafīs (d 1288), the Damascene physician al-Sāmirī (d 1282), the Persian physician Quṭb al-Dīn al-Šīrāsī, one Muḥammad ibn Maḥmūd al-Āmulī (d 1352) and others all wrote commentaries on the *Canon of medicine* in Arabic (Savage-Smith 2011: 242–68). These commentaries do not merely regurgitate previous medical knowledge, but also offer some new insights, as Ibn al-Nafīs' commentary on the first book of the *Canon*, known as *Book of generalities* (*Kitāb al-Kullīyāt*), shows. In it, he famously discovered the pulmonary transit, the fact that the blood moves from the right to the left ventricle of the heart via the lungs (where we now know that the blood is oxidised). Earlier anatomists, among them the great Galen (d *c*216), had thought that there was a small opening in the septum (the wall between the ventricles of the heart) through which the blood passed.

Further reading

Pormann (2013a) offers an up-to-date overview of work on Avicenna's medical output with further references; it also contains new interpretations, some of which have been summarised here. Fancy (2013) reads Ibn al-Nafīs' anatomical discoveries in the context of his overarching philosophy and theology; he shows that Ibn al-Nafīs' innovation is not restricted to the pulmonary transit.

Exhibition items

> No 5 (MSTR12): medieval manuscript of Avicenna's *Canon of medicine*

This is the oldest dated manuscript of the *Canon* at the RCP. This manuscript has a colophon, that is, a remark by the scribe at the end of the book about how he wrote it. It contains precious information and runs as follows:

> This is the end of the first book of the *Canon of Medicine*, dealing with the general principles. Praise be to God, as it is right and just. May God's prayers and blessings be upon our Lord Muḥammad, his Chosen Prophet, and upon his family.
>
> ᶜAlī ibn al-Ḥasan ibn al-Musāᶜid finished writing it at the end of Ǧumādā II in the year 611 (ie in early November AD 1214) in the City of Peace, Baghdad. Praise be to God in the beginning and in the end, both publicly and privately.

Therefore, we learn when the manuscript was written (early November 1214), and where, namely in the City of Peace, as Baghdad was then known. But the colophon also tells us something about the content of the manuscript: it contains only the first book (out of five) that make up the *Canon of medicine*. This book deals with the *Generalities* (*al-Kullīyāt*), or, as our scribe puts it, with the 'general principles' (*al-aḥkām al-kullīya*). There are, however, some minor lacunae in the manuscript, owing to the loss of certain folios.

The first book containing the *Generalities* is carefully divided and subdivided by Avicenna. It consists of four *fann*s, and each *fann* is further subdivided, but each in different ways. The first *fann* 'on the definition of medicine', for instance, is divided into six 'instructions' (*taᶜlīms*), and each instruction consists of a number of 'chapters' (*fuṣūl*), or 'summaries' (*ǧumlas*), or both. To give just two examples: Avicenna discusses the faculty of estimation (mentioned above) in book one, *fann* one, instruction six, summary one, chapter five 'on the cognitive psychic faculties' (*fī l-quwā al-nafsānīyati l-mudrikati*); and he discusses the venous artery (*al-širyān al-warīdī*) in book one, *fann* one, instruction five, summary four, chapter two. We shall return to the latter chapter in the next two entries, but it is interesting briefly to look at the former.

In the section on the cognitive psychic faculties, Avicenna describes estimation in the following terms (tr Pormann 2013a: 106):

> It [estimation (*wahm*)] is the faculty in the animal that judges that a wolf is an enemy, whereas a child is a loved one, and that the person who promises fodder is a friend from whom one does not flee – and this in a non-rational way. Enmity and friendship cannot be perceived, nor does sensation of the animal comprehend them. Therefore, it must be a different faculty that judges and comprehends them, even if this is not an act of rational comprehension (*al-idrāk an-nuṭqī*). It must therefore, by necessity, be a certain act of comprehension that is not rational. This faculty (estimation) is different from imagination (*al-ḫayāl*), because imagination regards the objects of sensation as authentic, whereas this [faculty, ie, estimation] makes judgments about the objects of sensation through concepts that are not objects of sensation. It [the faculty of estimation] also differs from that called 'thinking' (*al-mufakkira*) and 'imaginative' (*al-mutaḫayyila*) [faculties] insofar as the actions of the latter are not followed by any judgment, whereas the actions of the former are followed by a certain judgment, or even judgments. The actions of the former are composed of objects of sensation, whereas the action of the latter is a judgment about an object of sensation on the basis of a concept that goes beyond sensation.

This quotation shows (as already mentioned) that Avicenna introduces new philosophical concepts into his *Canon of medicine*. Therefore, we can see that the *Canon of medicine* not only summarises previous knowledge in a tightly organised hierarchy. It also contains innovations.

> No 6 (Oxford, Bodleian Library, MS Arab e177): early modern manuscript of Ibn al-Nafīs' *Commentary on the anatomy of the canon*

This is a 17th- or 18th-century manuscript containing the *Commentary on the anatomy of the canon* (*Šarḥ tašrīḥ al-Qānūn*) by Ibn al-Nafīs (d 1288). Avicenna mainly treats the subject of anatomy in two places in his *Canon of medicine*. First, he has a long section on this topic in the first book (called *Generalities*), namely in *fann* one, instruction (*taʿlīm*) five. Second, in book three, Avicenna discusses diseases occurring at a specific part of the body, from the head to the reproductive organs. Here he often provides information about the anatomy (*tašrīḥ*) of the various affected part of the body. In his *Commentary on the anatomy of the canon*, Ibn al-Nafīs explains these sections on anatomy from both book one and book three. Moreover, he also wrote a commentary on the other parts of the first book (see **no 7**).

When explaining the chapter about the venous artery in the *Canon*, Ibn al-Nafīs also deals with the problem of how the blood moves from the right to the left ventricle of the heart, challenging previous authorities. He first establishes that it is necessary for the blood to move from the right to the left ventricle (or chamber) of the heart, for blood is made thinner in the right ventricle and it produces pneuma in the left ventricle.

Then he famously says that 'there is no passage between the two [ventricles of the heart]' (*laysa baynahumā [taǧwīfayi l-qalbi] manfaḏun*). He then argues that the blood must pass through the lungs where the thinner blood is mixed with air and then passes to the left ventricle of the heart; the thicker blood is used to nourish the lungs. He finishes with a short teleological description of the arterial vein (that is, the pulmonary artery in modern terminology) and the venous artery (that is, the pulmonary vein). Here is Ibn al-Nafīs' explanation in his own words:

> We are now going to say the following, although God knows best. Since one of the functions of the heart is to generate pneuma – the functions being brought about by very thin blood that is strongly mixed with the mass of the air – it is necessary that very thin blood and air be produced in the heart, so that pneuma can be produced from the mass mixed of the two [ie thin blood and air]. Moreover, the pneuma is generated in the left of the two ventricles of the heart.
>
> It is [therefore] necessary that in the heart of humans and other similar beings who have lungs there be another ventricle in which the blood becomes thinner, so that it is able to mix with the air. For if the air were mixed with the blood whilst it is thick, then the union of the two [ie blood and air] would not produce a homoeomerous body. This ventricle is the right of the two ventricles of the heart. When the blood becomes thinner in this ventricle, it is necessary that it pass into the left ventricle where the pneuma is generated. But there is no passage between the two [ventricles]. For the body of the heart is uniform there: it has neither a visible passage, as some people have thought, nor an invisible passage through which this blood could pass, as Galen had imagined. For the pores of the heart there are firm and its body thick. Therefore, when this blood has become thin, it must necessarily pass through the arterial vein to the lungs. It is then spread through the body of the lungs and mixed with air. Its thinnest part is filtered out, and passes to the venous artery, so that it [the venous artery] brings it [the blood] to the left of the two ventricles of the heart. It has previously been mixed with air and is now capable of generating the pneuma. The remainder of the blood is used by the lungs for nourishment. It is for this reason that the arterial vein is made firm, having two layers, so that its pores that are penetrated are extremely thin, whereas the venous artery is made thin, having just one layer, so that it [venous artery] can easily absorb what comes out of this [arterial] vein. For this reason, there are perceptible passages between these two blood vessels.

In other words, Ibn al-Nafīs establishes that the blood must pass from the right to the left ventricle of the heart via the lungs, thus refuting Galen and others who assumed that there was a passage in the septum.

This short text was first discovered by an Egyptian physician working in Berlin in the 1924, called Muḥyī l-Dīn al-Ṭaṭāwī, and given much greater publicity in an article written by Max Meyerhof (1935b). It is perhaps the most quoted example of medical innovation in the Arabo-Islamic world. But unfortunately, the exact nature of this discovery is often overstated. Meyerhof had already talked about the 'lesser circulation' of blood, insinuating that Ibn al-Nafīs knew that blood circulated, but this is not actually true. Ibn al-Nafīs never talks about circulation, but only about the passage of blood via the lungs, or, to use a modern term, the pulmonary transit. The blood that remains in the lungs is expended there for nourishment. Likewise the blood that passes from the left ventricle of the heart to the rest of the body is expended there; it does not return to the right ventricle according to Ibn al-Nafīs. This does not detract from the importance of this discovery, but one should avoid talking of 'lesser circulation' in this context. (See also Fancy 2013, ch 5, for a detailed discussion.)

> No 7 (MSTR21): a manuscript of Ibn al-Nafīs' *Commentary on the generalities of the canon*

This manuscript contains the 'second volume' (*al-muǧallada al-ṯāniya*) of Ibn al-Nafīs' *Commentary on the generalities of the canon*. It begins with a discussion of the faculties, corresponding to book one, *fann* one, instruction five, summary five of the *Canon*.

Ibn al-Nafīs arranged this commentary in a lemmatic format. This means that he first quoted a passage from the *Canon*, known as a 'lemma'. In our manuscript, these lemmas appear as rubrics, that is, they are written in red, whereas Ibn al-Nafīs' explanations are written in black ink (see **fig 2.2**). He then explains the lemma and comments on it. In the case of this commentary, however, the lemmas are often not complete, but only include the beginning and the end of the text on which Ibn al-Nafīs comments; it is as if he used three dots '...' to indicate an omission in the middle. The reader is supposed to have access to the full text of the *Canon*, either from a copy or from memory. Furthermore, he only discusses sections from the *Generalities* (*al-Kullīyāt*, ie the first book of the *Canon*) that do not deal with anatomy; the anatomical sections are discussed in his *Commentary on the anatomy of the canon* (*Šarḥ tašrīḥ al-Qānūn*; **no 6**).

In the introduction to this chapter, we saw that Avicenna includes his innovative philosophical ideas in his medical works. Ibn al-Nafīs also saw this. **Fig 2.2** shows his discussion of estimation, where he comments on the following passage in Avicenna's *Canon*: 'This faculty (imagination) serves as an instrument (*āla*) for a faculty that really is the internal cognitive [one] in the living being, namely estimation (*wahm*).' After quoting this passage, Ibn al-Nafīs cites the corresponding discussion from book (*maqāla*) four, chapter (*faṣl*) one of the section on Physics (*Ṭabīᶜīyāt*) of Avicenna's philosophical encyclopaedia *The cure* (*Al-Šifāʾ*) on psychology (*ᶜilm al-nafs*). In other words, Ibn al-Nafīs himself compares what

Fig 2.2, no 7 *Commentary on Avicenna's generalities of the canon*, Ibn al-Nafīs.

Avicenna says in his philosophical encyclopaedia (*The cure*) with what he argues in his medical encyclopaedia (*The canon of medicine*). He comes to this conclusion: 'This [the quotation from *The cure*] is [also] the text at this place. It agrees with what he [Avicenna] said in the *Canon*, and does not conflict with what was said [there].' To put it differently: Ibn al-Nafīs was fully aware that Avicenna included his philosophical ideas in his main medical work. In this sense, he was certainly ahead of some modern scholars studying the *Canon*.

> No 8 (MS385): medieval manuscript of the Latin translation of Avicenna's *Canon*

This is a Latin manuscript probably dating back to the 14th century that contains the first book of Avicenna's *Canon of medicine* in the translation of Gerard of Cremona. The manuscript itself was probably written in Italy, although the binding appears to have been produced in Germany in the 16th century.

Like the Arabic manuscript on display (**no 5**), it only contains the first book, the *Generalities*. This is obviously not an accident, as this first book proved to be particularly popular. From it, the student, for instance, could learn the basic facts about the human body as well as the how medicine worked.

This particular manuscript has an interesting provenance. Produced in Italy in the 14th century and rebound in Germany in the 16th, it was purchased by the antiquarian and collector Sir Thomas Phillipps (1792–1872). He came from Manchester, but studied in London, where he developed his 'vello-mania' (or obsessive love for parchment manuscripts). Throughout his long life, he acquired an enormous collection, but he failed to provide adequately for it, so that it was sold piecemeal after his death. He bought this particular manuscript in 1836 for '£1 1s 0d', and it was sold at auction through Sotheby's in 1903 (Ker 1969: 216). The RCP purchased it as part of its acquisition strategy.

The Latin translation of the *Canon* by Gerard of Cremona remained popular throughout the Middle Ages. But in the early 16th century, it was replaced by a new translation prepared by Andrea Alpago of Belluno (d 1522; see Veit 2006). This Renaissance physician spent some 20 years in Damascus, where he worked for the Venetian consulate, only returning to Italy in 1517. During his time in the East, he learnt Arabic to an impressive level and became acquainted with Arabic medical and philosophical writings. His most enduring contribution is a revision and retranslation of Avicenna's *Canon*. But he also worked on a new translation of Ibn Sarābiyūn's *Small compendium* (Pormann 2004c). Because of his untimely death, both these translations were edited posthumously by his nephew, Paolo Alpago. Although the title pages of both translations make grandiose claims of being based on a collation of Arabic manuscripts or freshly translated into Arabic, it is clear that Andrea Alpago did not revise Gerard's translations with equal care everywhere. In fact, in the case of Ibn Sarābiyūn, Alpago's translation often amounts to little more than orthographical changes, and at least some of his explanations of rare words are based solely on the Latin version with no recourse to the Arabic (Pormann 2008d: 356–8). This said, the efforts of Andrea Alpago to improve Avicenna's translation of the *Canon* illustrate the great interest with which Renaissance scholars approach this seminal work. After all, it was mainly Alpago's revised translation that continued to be printed over and over again.

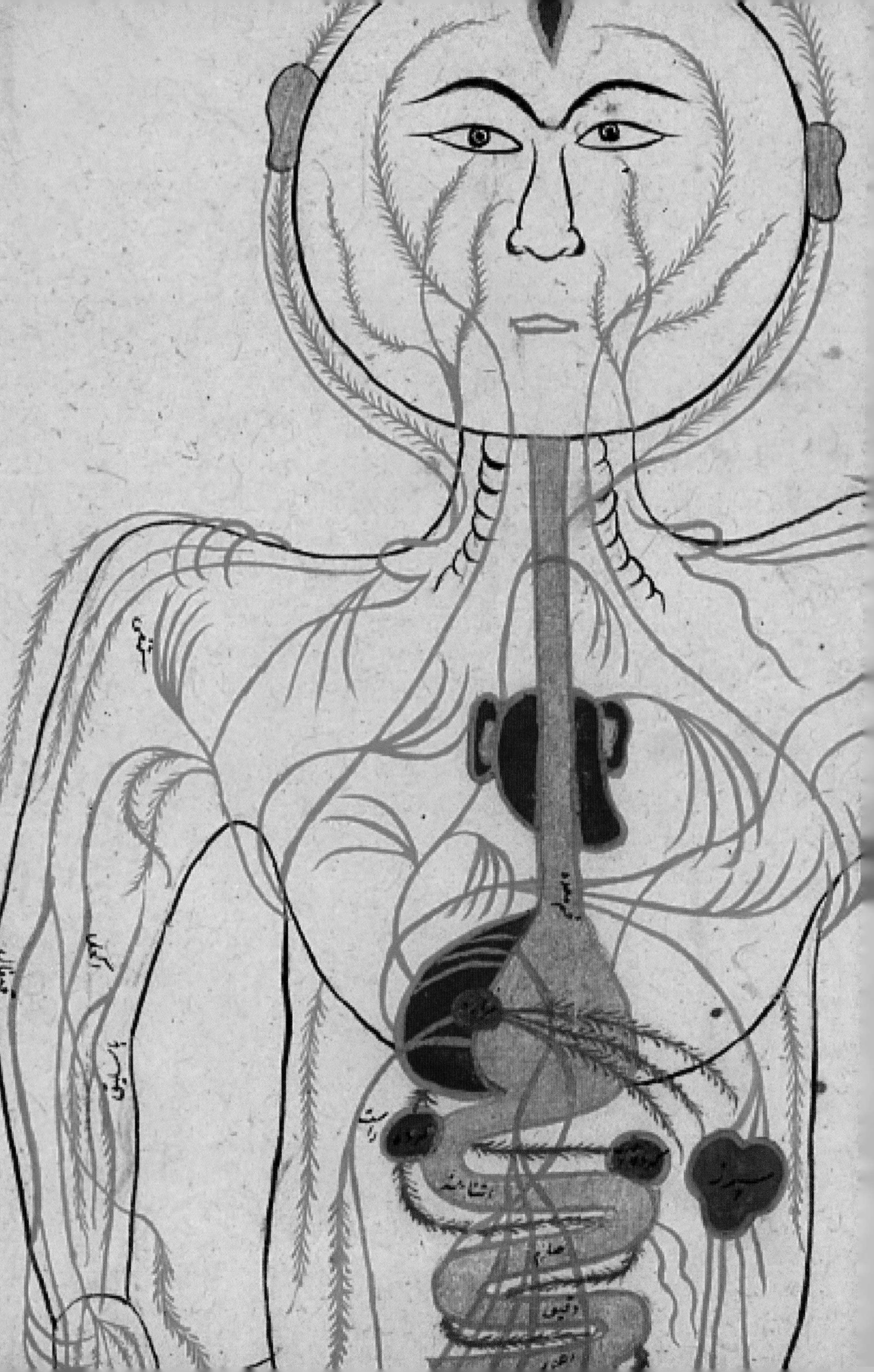

Fig 3.1 Veins and arteries, illustration from *Manṣūr's anatomy* (*Tašrīḥ-i Manṣūrī*), 1658 – detail.

من اشتغل بعلم التشريح ازداد إيمانا بالله

If one occupies oneself with the science of anatomy, one increases one's belief in God.
(Statement attributed to Ibn Rušd (Averroes, d 1198))

3 Anatomy: the unknown frontier

The term anatomy comes from the Greek word *anatomḗ*, which designates both anatomy in the modern sense of 'the science concerned with bodily structures', and dissection, that is, the cutting open of the dead (and sometimes living) body in order to study its structures. Like its Greek equivalent, Arabic *tašrīḥ* also has this double meaning of anatomy and dissection. Generally speaking, dissection was not practised in the medieval Islamic world; however, the reason for this was not a religious or societal taboo, but rather a lack of interest. As Emilie Savage-Smith (1995: 110) concluded (referencing GER Lloyd) in her seminal study of the topic, 'if... there was no particular anatomical problem to test, then there was little impetus to undertake the difficult and distasteful dissection and little if anything to be gained from the experience'.

But although dissection was not generally practised, the interest in anatomy was great, as the opening quotation by the famous Andalusian scholar Ibn Rušd (Averroes, d 1198) shows. The idea behind this quotation is a teleological view of anatomy, which one might also call the design argument: the functions of the various parts of our body are so complex and sophisticated that they reveal the great foresight and wisdom of the Creator. Galen had already concluded his main work on functional anatomy, *On the usefulness of the parts*, with a hymn to the demiurge (or creator of the universe).

Likewise, numerous physicians in the medieval Islamic world wrote on anatomy, continuing a tradition that started in the ancient Greek world. And we have already seen that they found new things, as did Ibn al-Nafīs who discovered the pulmonary transit (see **no 6**). Another instance of an inquisitive anatomical mind is that of ʿAbd al-Laṭīf al-Baġdādī: not satisfied with Galen's description of the mandible, he 'investigated it in many individuals, in over two thousand skulls in different ways' (*wa-ʿtabarnāhu mā šāʾa llāhu mina l-marrāti fī ašḫāṣin kaṯīratin tazīdu ʿalā alfay ǧumǧumatin bi-asnāfin mina l-iʿtibārāti*) (Zand, Videan 1964: 275). ʿAbd al-Laṭīf subsequently came to a different (and correct) conclusion, namely that the lower jawbone consists of one fused bone. Moreover ʿAbd al-Laṭīf also corrected Galen's description of the sacrum and the coccyx.

Illustrations form an integral part of modern anatomical writings. In the medieval Islamic world, we have to wait until the 14th century to find illustrations of the full human figure. The earliest illustrations are in fact geometrical drawings, for instance, of the jaw or cranial sutures (Savage-Smith 2007: 148–55). It would appear that Ḥunayn ibn Isḥāq is the first to illustrate the functional aspects of the eye in his *Ten treatises on the eye*, and later ophthalmological manuals not infrequently contain illustrations. But in the medieval Arabic medical literature as it is preserved today, there are no images of the whole human body. This is somewhat surprising, given that a Persian manual on anatomy, dating back to the 14th century, contains a series of such images.

This Persian manual (**no 9**) is *Manṣūr's anatomy* (*Tašrīḥ-i Manṣūrī*), a book written by Manṣūr ibn Muḥammad ibn Aḥmad ibn Yūsuf ibn Faqīh Ilyās in 1386 and dedicated to the ruler of the province Fars, called Pīr Muḥammad Bahādur Ḫān. It consists of five books (*maqālas*), dealing with bones, nerves, muscles, veins and arteries respectively; a concluding part deals with compound organs. This anatomical text is remarkable for its illustrations. For in many of the more than 60 manuscripts in which it is preserved, we find a series of images depicting different aspects of the full human figure, namely the skeleton, the nervous system, the muscles, the veins, the arteries and a pregnant woman.

Generally speaking Manṣūr relied heavily in his *Anatomy* on Arabic sources, and much of the anatomical nomenclature remains Arabic. It is therefore surprising that no Arabic source for the illustrations has yet been found. The situation is further complicated by the fact that a number of Western manuscripts have similar figures. Among the oldest are two Latin manuscripts: a miscellany (that is, a manuscript containing different texts) from the 12th century, now kept at Gonville and Caius College, Cambridge (**no 10**); and another miscellany dated to 1293, now in the Bodlian Library, Oxford (**no 11**). It is possible to compare the version of the Manṣūr illustrations contained in the manuscript of the RCP (**no 9**) with these two Latin manuscripts. Let us do this figure by figure (**Figs 3.2 to 3.5**).

When looking at the figures showing the skeleton, one is at once struck both by their similarity and differences. The Latin manuscripts depict the bones inside a fairly fleshy human being, whereas the Persian one is extremely schematic. The second major difference is the perspective. In the Manṣūr illustration we view the skeleton from the back, with the palms turned towards us. The head owes its strange appearance to the fact that it is hyper-extended: as if we move with a camera from behind over the head to the face, creating one image. Yet the squatting position is very similar, especially when we compare the Gonville and Caius manuscript to the Manṣūr.

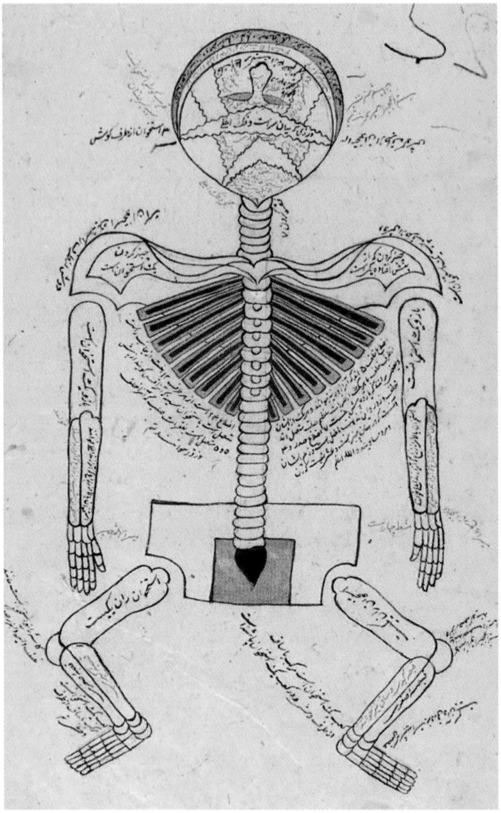

Fig 3.2a, no 9 Skeleton, illustration from *Manṣūr's anatomy* (*Tašrīḥ-i Manṣūrī*), 1656.

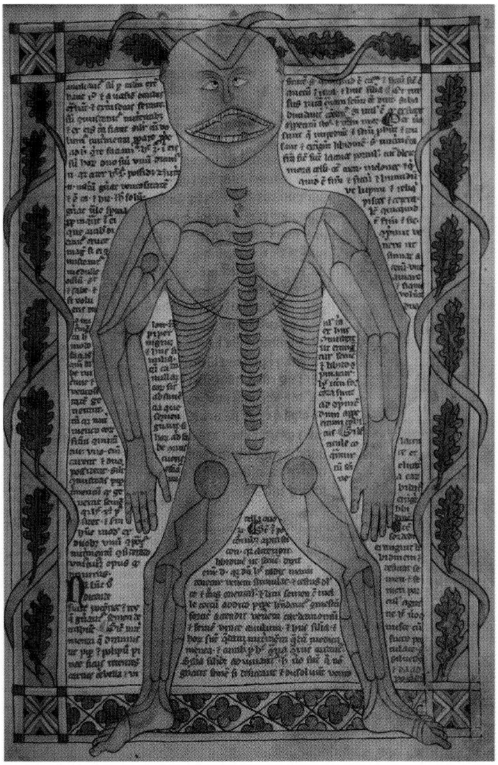

Fig 3.2c, no 11 Skeleton, illustration from ***The fabric of the human body***, c1292 © Bodleian Library, Oxford.

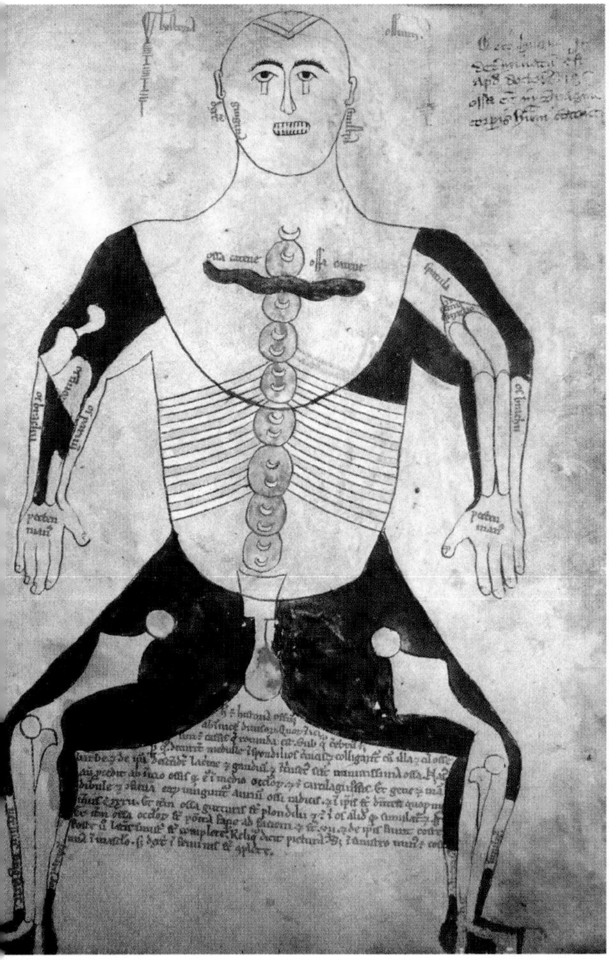

Fig 3.2b, no 10 Bone system (*historia ossium*), illustration from a medieval medical miscellany © Gonville and Caius College, Cambridge.

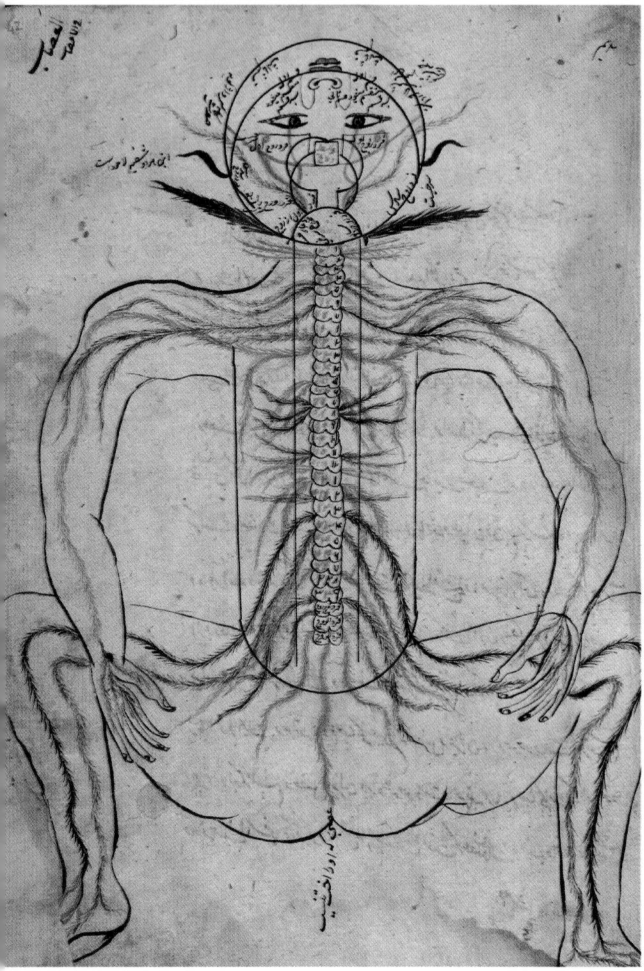

Fig 3.3a, no 9 Nerves, illustration from *Manṣūr's anatomy* (*Tašrīḥ-i Manṣūrī*), 1656.

In the case of the figure illustrating the nerves, we find a similar pattern: the two Latin illuminations are much closer to each other, displaying the main nerves only. They are drawn so as to show the face and the front of the body. The Manṣūr figure offers a far greater amount of detail: types of nerves are distinguished by colour (green, olive, yellowish, red, blue and pink). The head is again hyperextended from the rear, and the upper body also appears from the rear; however, the lower body with the legs is drawn from the front, so as to present a strange, even contorted image of a human being.

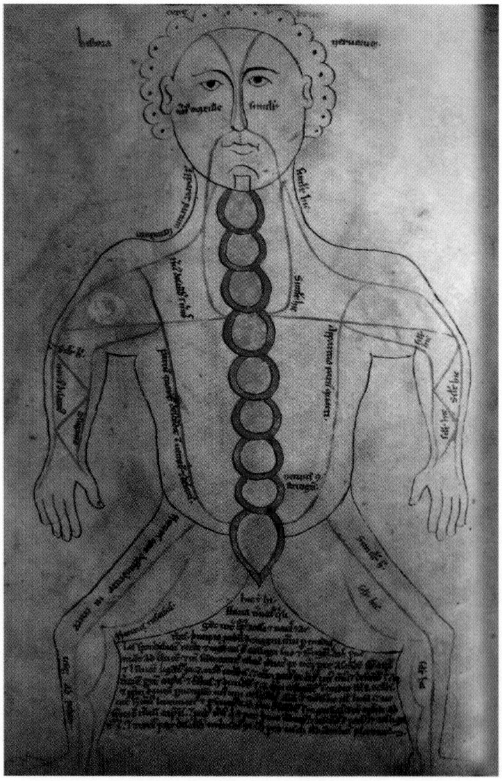

Fig 3.3b, no 10 Nervous system, illustration from a medieval medical miscellany © Gonville and Caius College, Cambridge.

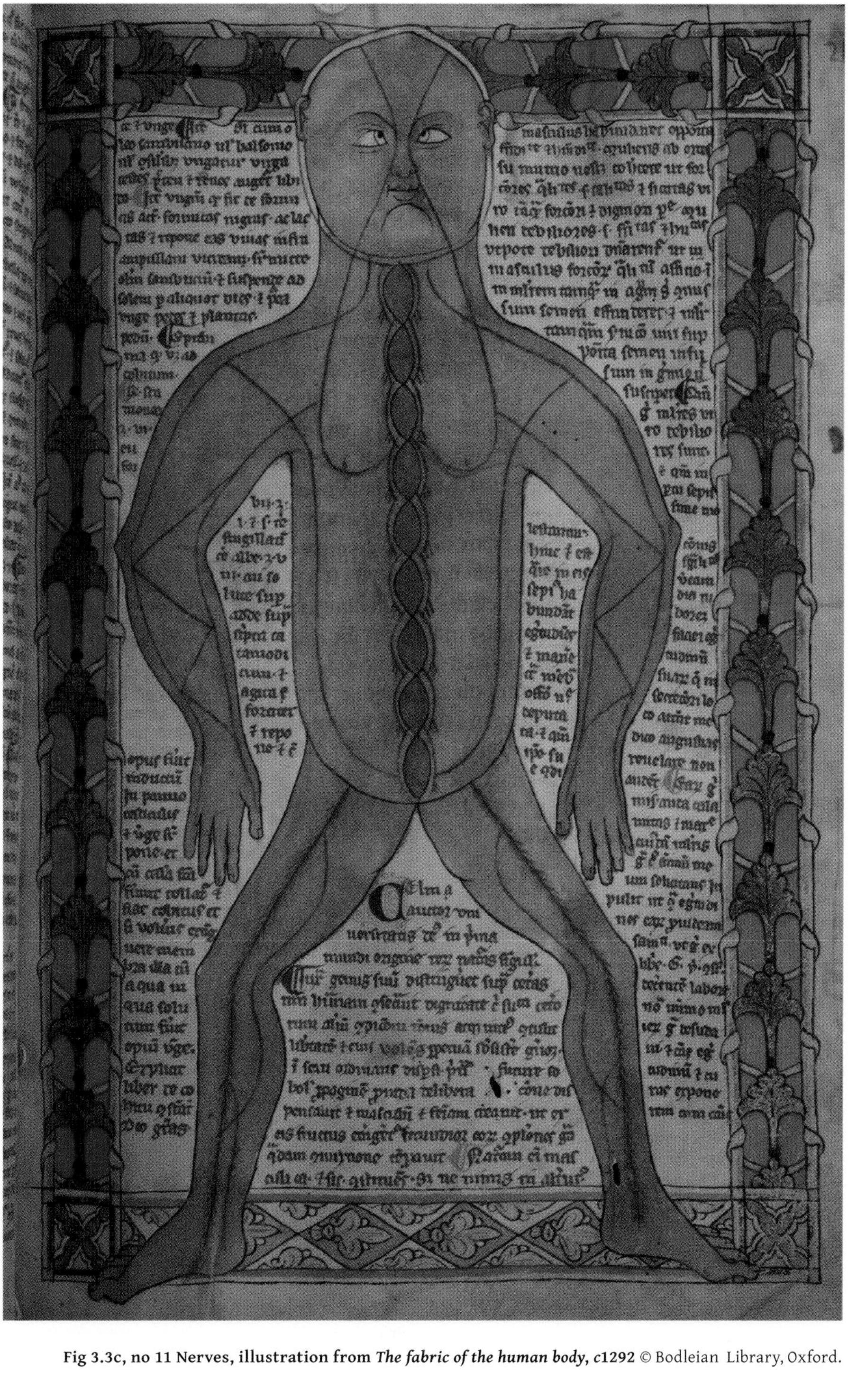

Fig 3.3c, no 11 Nerves, illustration from *The fabric of the human body*, c1292 © Bodleian Library, Oxford.

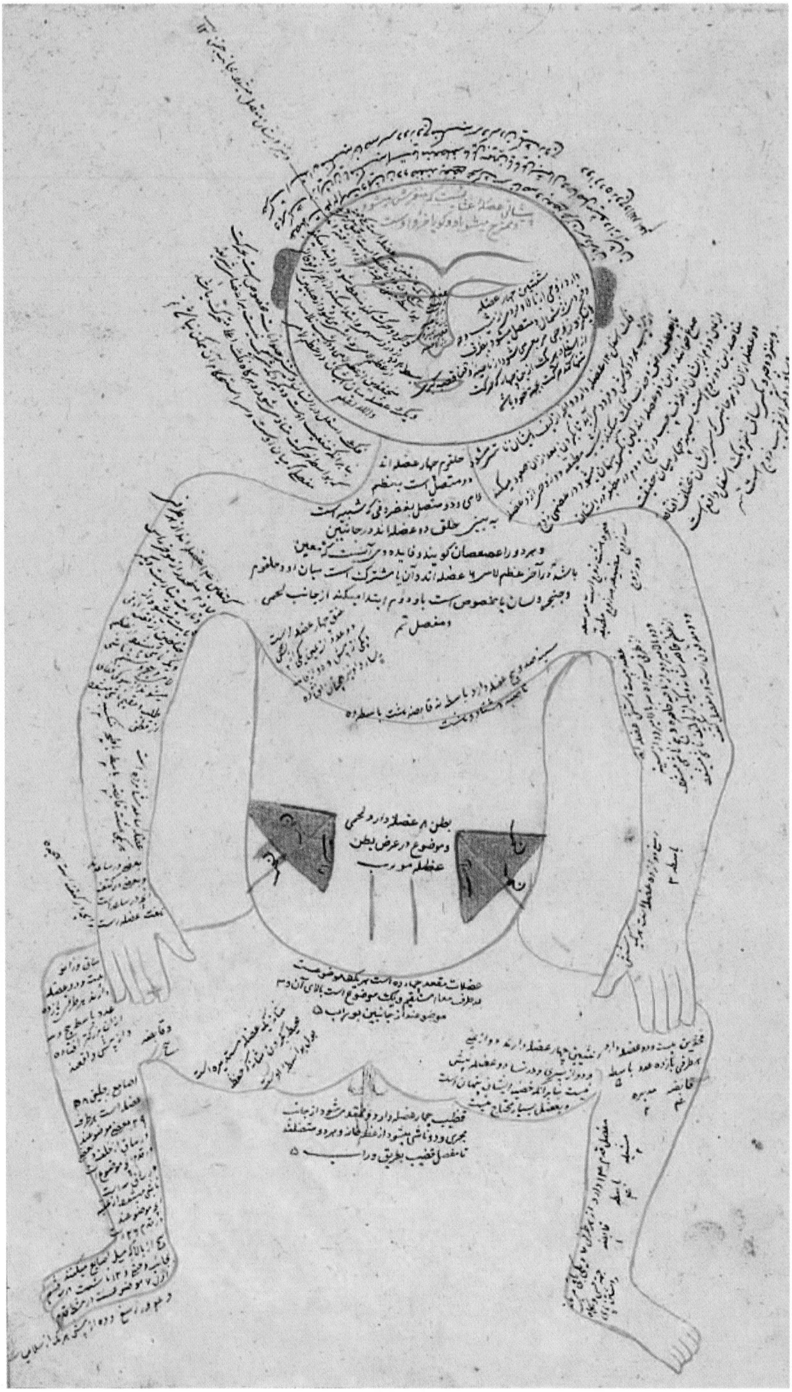

Fig 3.4a, no 9 Muscles, illustration from *Manṣūr's anatomy* (*Tašrīḥ-i Manṣūrī*), 1656.

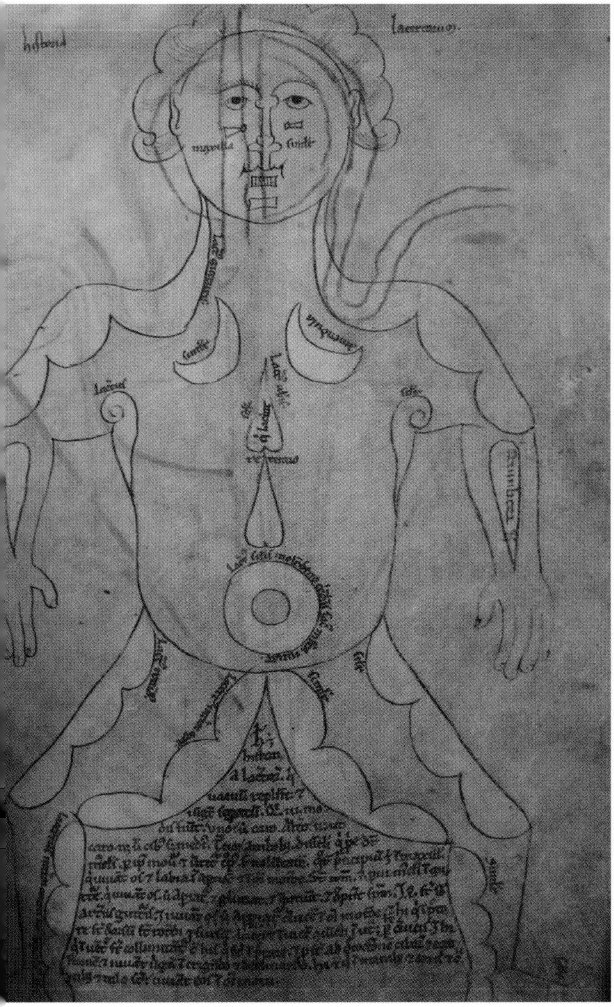

Fig 3.4b, no 10 Muscular system (*historia lacertorum*), illustration from a medieval medical miscellany

For the illustration of the muscles, the Manṣūr figure faces us, sitting again in a squatting position with the hands placed on the thighs. The corresponding Latin illuminations have quite a similar appearance, and both in the Gonville and Caius manuscript and the Manṣūr manuscript, the shoulders are higher than the arms. The triangles that are visible in the Manṣūr figure's lower abdomen represent the stomach muscles.

We encounter such geometric depictions also in the Arabic tradition, such as a manuscript of the *Explanation of causes and signs* (*Šarḥ al-asbāb wa-l-ʿalāmāt*) by Burhān al-Dīn Nafīs ibn ʿIwāḍ al-Kirmānī (d 1449), court physician to Uluġ Bēg (Savage-Smith 2007: 149). In the Gonville and Caius manuscript, the figure is entitled 'Account of the muscular parts of the arms' (*historia lacertorum*), but this is clearly a metonymy for the whole system of the muscles, as the muscles not only in the legs, but also the main body are displayed.

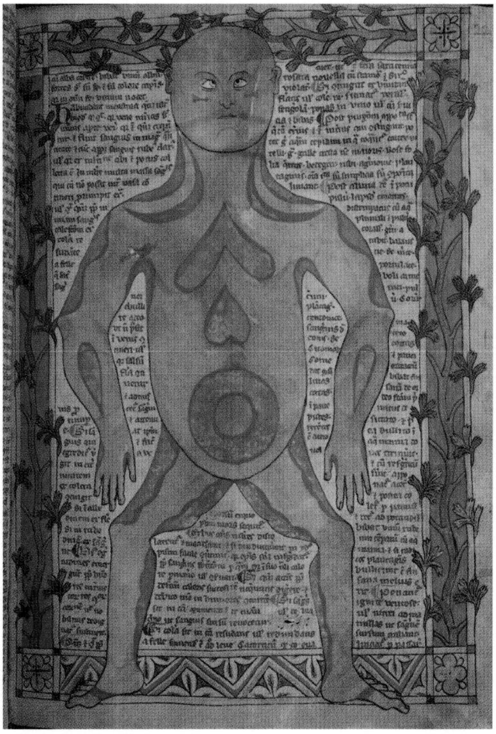

Fig 3.4c, no 11 Muscles, illustration from *The fabric of the human body*, c1292

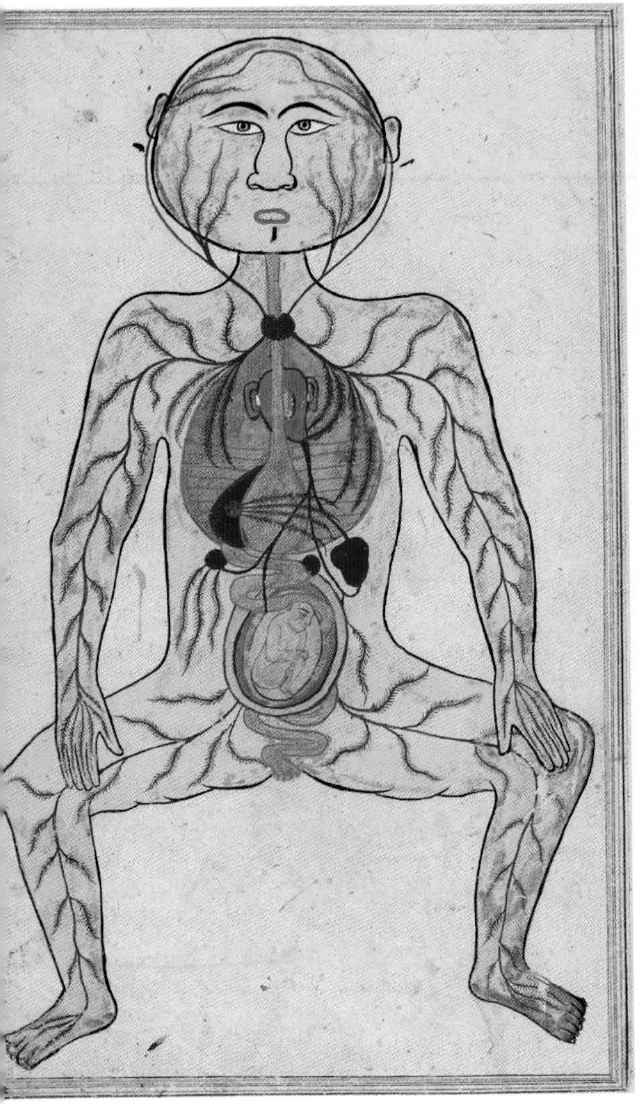

Fig 3.5a, no 9 Female reproduction, illustration from *Manṣūr's anatomy* (*Tašrīḥ-i Manṣūrī*), 1656.

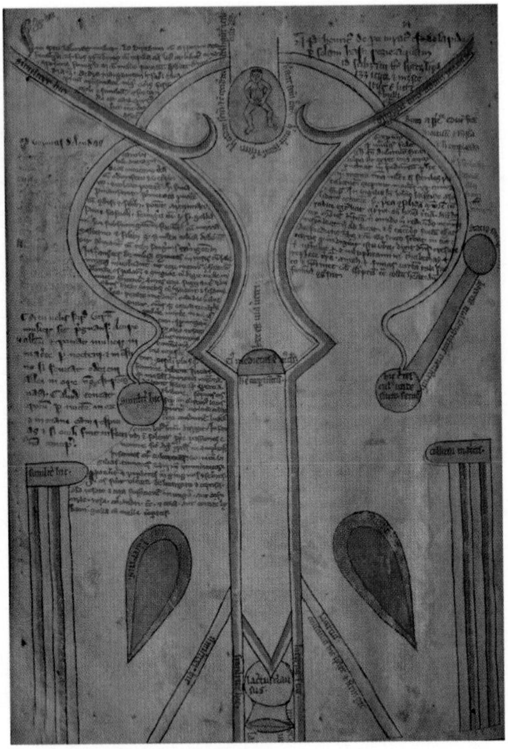

Fig 3.5b, no 11 Female reproduction, illustration from *The fabric of the human body*, c1292

The five images of the bones, nerves, muscles, veins and arteries have clear corresponding images in the Latin tradition. The sixth image in the Manṣūr manuscript – that of the pregnant woman with the fetus – does not, however. Emilie Savage-Smith (2011: 155–6) has therefore cautiously suggested that '[t]he figure with gravid uterus was...the only contribution that Ibn Ilyās himself made to anatomical illustration, for all the other elements were...taken from earlier sources'. The image shows a pregnant woman in the squatting position. Apart from the womb with the fetus, the image resembles the previous Manṣūr image illustrating the veins and arteries. In fact, some of the organs and blood vessels are drawn in nearly the same way.

In the Bodleian Ashmole manuscript, we do find a rather geometrical depiction of the fetus in the womb and the act of sexual penetration. This image, however, is rather different from the Manṣūr one. We see the female womb and vagina on the top, with the womb containing a childlike fetus. In the lower part, a penis penetrates the vagina, and the testicles are also represented. Legends explain what happens: on top of the penis, for instance, we read 'This is the way to the womb' (*haec est uia uteri*). But despite their dissimilarity, the two images share the fact that the fetus resembles a person that has already been born and grown for some years.

This detailed comparison between the images in the Manṣūr and the Latin manuscripts shows that the similarities between them go far beyond coincidence. How, then, do we explain this? In temporal terms, the Latin manuscripts predate the Persian treatise by at least 100 years, and in the case of the oldest ones, even more than 200 years. One might follow the logic of *post hoc ergo propter hoc*, meaning that just because A occurs *after* B, A is therefore also *caused* by B. In our case, this would mean that because Manṣūr lived some 200 years after the Latin manuscripts were written, he must therefore have somehow drawn on them, either directly or indirectly. This argument, however, is highly unlikely. There was no translation, directly or indirectly, of medical texts from Latin into Persian at that time, and the Arabised vocabulary of *Manṣūr's anatomy* points not to a Latin, but to an Arabic source text. If one excludes coincidence and the Latin-Persian transmission as possibilities, then there remain two other plausible explanations. The first is that of a common Arabic source. In this scenario, an Arabic treatise with anatomical illustrations that is now lost must have circulated by the early 12th century at the latest. It then became known in Latin in the wake of the Arabo-Latin translation movement that, as we saw, already begun in the 11th century. Although the exact modalities of transmission remain illusive, this scenario would make good sense. The second possibility is a common late antique (Greek) source. In this case, the Greek model would have crossed the language barrier possibly sometime between the 6th and the 10th century in Italy, where many medical texts from late antiquity were rendered from Greek into Latin. Likewise, the Greek model would have been transmitted into Arabic in the context of the Graeco-Arabic translation movement. This scenario is less satisfying, because it would not explain why no-one took notice of the anatomical images for such a long period of time, both in Latin and in Arabic. But even if one accepts the first scenario, one still wonders why this presumed Arabic source did not leave any trace.

Further reading

The seminal study on attitudes towards dissection in the medieval Islamic world remains Savage-Smith (1995). Likewise, Savage-Smith (2007) has produced the authoritative treatment of anatomical illustrations in medieval Islamic manuscripts. Both articles provide further references.

Exhibition items

> **No 9** (MSTR46): 17th-century manuscript of *Manṣūr's anatomy*

This copy of *Manṣūr's anatomy* (*Tašrīḥ-i Manṣūrī*) is dated to AD 1656. It was donated to the RCP by Roy Dobbin (see below, chapter 9). For a detailed discussion of its content and importance, see pp29–37.

> **No 10** (Cambridge, Gonville and Caius, MS190/223, CMA 1107): medieval Latin medical miscellany

This is a composite manuscript, consisting of two main parts (James 1907–8: i. 218–19). The first part contains the famous 10 drawings with accompanying text of: (1) the arterial system (*istoria arteriarum*); (2) the veinal system (*historia uenarum*); (3) the bone system (*historia ossium*); (4) the nervous system (*historia neruorum*); (5) the muscular system (*historia lacertorum*); (6) a section on the lower abdomen; (7) the internal organs; (8) another section on the lower abdomen; (9) the eyes and the nose; and (10) diagrams illustrating the elements, mixtures and so forth. We have already discussed numbers 1 and 3 to 5 in detail above.

The second part is later than the first, dating to the 15th century. It includes a treatise on prostate cancer (*ad cancrum in uirga uirili*) by 'M Joh. Arderne', followed by various recipes and shorter medical texts in both English and Latin. This manuscript forms part of a group of roughly 150 manuscripts given to Gonville and Caius College by one of its former fellows, the librarian and collector William Moore (*c*1590–1659).

> **No 11** (Oxford, Bodleian Library, MS Ashmole 399): composite medieval Latin manuscript, containing medical, philosophical, hermetic, mathematical and astrological texts

This manuscript is remarkable for two main reasons. First, it contains a series of illuminations depicting the human body and various organs; we have already discussed their similarity to the anatomical drawings contained in *Manṣūr's anatomy*. Moreover, throughout the rest of the volume there are some quite stunning illuminations. Second, it shows the diverse interests of scribes and scholars in the Latin West, as it deals with a broad variety of subjects, which would all have come under the heading of 'science' (*scientia*). The following list provides some short descriptions (based on Black 1845: 313–17).

1 A book on physiognomy (*Liber de Physiognomia*) by an anonymous author, written in 1152.

2 A treatise on obstetrics, dealing with the shape of the womb, the various positions of the fetus in it, and also the formation of the fetus (*Tractatus obstetricius de forma uteri, et fetus in eo positionibus diversis; etiam de fetus formatione*).

3 A short treatise on chiromancy.

4 A calendar in tabular form, arranged according to dominical letters and the Moon's cycle (*Calendarium tabulare, ad literas dominicales et cyclum lunarem accommodatum*).

5 A book about the fabric of the human body, with pictures (*Liber de corporis humani fabrica, cum picturis*); this is where the anatomical illustrations occur (**Figs 3.2c, 3.3c, 3.4c, 3.5b**).

6 A table illustrating the Moon's cycle, the dominical letters and the Easter days, for the years 1001–29, 1100, 1118, 1200, 1292–1531 (*Tabula monstrans cyclum lunarem, literas dominicales et dies paschales, per annos* 1001–29, 1118, 1200, 1292–1531); it was apparently written in 1292.

7 Constantine the African's book on sexual intercouse (*Liber de coitu*).

8 Book on the diseases of women, especially those arising from childbirth, mainly compiled from the writings of Galen, Hippocrates and Constantine (the African) (*Liber de aegritudinibus Mulierum, et maxime de liberorum partu, e Galeni, Hippocratis, et Constantini libris plerumque confectus*).

9 Jottings about the formation of the fetus (*Scriptiuncula de formatione fetus*).

10 A booklet on anatomy (*Libellus de Anatomia*).

11 Constantine the African's book on the stomach (*Constantini liber de Stomacho*).

12 John of Saint Paul's booklet on simple drugs (*Johannis de Sancto Paulo libellus de simplicibus medicinis*).

13 A list of substitute drugs entitled *Quid pro quo.*

14 A short poem on uroscopy.

15 Book of the fates of the 28 judges (*Liber 28 Judicum Fatorum*).

16 Spells through names, according to the number of letters (*Sortes per nomina, secundum numerum literarum*).

17 Another treatise on chiromancy.

18 Treatise on the pulse (*Tractatus de Pulsibus*).

19 Poem on arithmetics (*Carmen de Arithmetica*).

20 A treatise on algorithms.

We therefore have medicine placed next to mathematics, divination next to tabular calendars, and some magic as well.

Fig 4.1 Bronze mortar © Science Museum.

Je ne crois pas qu'il soit possible de porter l'art de guérir la petite vérole, sur-tout dans le premier état, au point de perfection où est parvenu Rhasès.

I do not think it possible to bring the art of healing small-pox – especially in its initial state – to the same level of perfection as that achieved by al-Rāzī.

4 al-Rāzī, the clinician

The above quotation is the judgement of the French physician Jean-Jacques Paulet (1740–1826) about al-Rāzī's treatise, *On smallpox and measles* (Paulet 1768: vi). Here, a practising doctor in Enlightenment Montpellier acknowledges the great skill that al-Rāzī had as a clinician. And he certainly was right in doing so. Yet who was this author whose medical works stood the test of time for nearly a millennium?

Abū Bakr Muḥammad ibn Zakarīyāʾ al-Rāzī (*c*865–925) came from the city of Rayy (near modern Teheran), but spent a large part of his formative years and subsequent career as a physician in Baghdad. He wrote profusely not only on medicine, but also on philosophy. His views about God and his creation, however, were considered heretical by both contemporaneous and subsequent thinkers, and most of his philosophical œuvre is therefore lost (Daiber 2012). His medical works, however, have come down to us, and anecdotal evidence suggests that al-Rāzī continued to enjoy court patronage because of his great clinical aptitude, which perhaps reconciled some with his more heretical doctrines.

Be that as it may, we can form an excellent opinion both of al-Rāzī as a clinician and as a medical author because numerous medical works by him survive. The most important ones are the following.

> The *Book for al-Manṣūr* (*al-Kitāb al-Manṣūrī*), a medical encyclopaedia in 10 books. Although this is a medical handbook in the tradition of the medical encyclopaedias of late antiquity such as that composed by Paul of Aegina, it still contains some novelties and innovations. One famous example includes an animal experiment. In order to test the idea that mercury is relatively harmless when swallowed, al-Rāzī administers mercury to an ape and observes the effects. Although the ape obviously feels pain, it passes the mercury and continues to live (Pormann 2008c: 111–12). It proved extremely popular, and was translated into Latin (cf **no 15**) and Hebrew. Vesalius also wrote an abridgment of it (**no 14**).

> A short treatise, *On smallpox and measles* (*Fī l-ǧudarī wa-l-ḥaṣba*), which distinguishes between two diseases that were either conflated in the previous Greek tradition or unknown. It proved incredibly popular in the West, and was translated into Syriac, Greek, Latin (repeatedly), English and French.

- The *Doubts about Galen* (*Kitāb al-Šukūk ᶜalā Ǧālīnūs*), a book in which al-Rāzī criticises Galen on numerous points. Some aspects of this book deal with philosophical topics such as the nature of the soul. Is it material or not? Does it survive the death and decay of the body? But al-Rāzī also insists on his practical experience, notably in various hospitals in both Baghdad and Rayy (Pormann 2008c). It therefore shows al-Rāzī not only as a shrewd physician, but also as a keen clinician.

- The *Comprehensive book* (*al-Kitāb al-Ḥāwī*), a massive collection of notes published posthumously by his students. Throughout his long professional life, al-Rāzī took notes; he read virtually all the medical literature available at the time and excerpted the main points of interest. After his death, his students gathered these notes together and collected them into one massive work (comprising 23 volumes in the modern Hyderabad printing). Therefore, a lot of these notes consist of quotations and paraphrases of various previous medical texts, many of them Greek. As such, this collection is incredibly important, as it allows us to recover the writings of lost works such as Rufus of Ephesus' book, *On melancholy* (Pormann 2008a). Yet, we also find many of his comments interspersed throughout this massive work, as well as a section with 33 case notes (Meyerhof 1935a). Therefore, the *Comprehensive book* offers interesting insights into al-Rāzī's clinical practice, and not only his reading habits. A famous example comes from the section on brain fever (*sirsām*, corresponding to Greek *phrenîtis*): here, al-Rāzī tested a treatment (bloodletting) by using a control group. This allowed him to come to the conclusion that bloodletting is an effective treatment against brain fever (Pormann 2008c: 109–11; Iskandar 2011: 225–6). Although we would no longer recognise this treatment as effective, the use of a control group marks significant methodological progress. Finally, it should be noted that the *Comprehensive book* (*al-Kitāb al-Ḥāwī*) is essentially the same work as that to which al-Rāzī himself refers as the 'Collective' [Book] (*al-Ǧāmiᶜ*), or the 'Great collective book' (*al-Ǧāmiᶜ al-kabīr*) (Savage-Smith 2012).

- The *Book of experiences* (*Kitāb al-Taǧārib*). The 33 case histories contained in al-Rāzī's *Comprehensive book* are by no means the only notes recording his cases. In fact, students kept case notes for al-Rāzī and they collected them and published them posthumously as the *Book of experiences* (Álvarez-Millán 2000, 2010). These case notes are a precious source for knowing how al-Rāzī actually treated patients, as opposed to how he described various treatments in the learned literature. This problem of medical history, which one may call the theory versus practice debate, is an extremely interesting one. Álvarez-Millán (2000), for instance, has shown that al-Rāzī records many complicated recipes and treatments for ophthalmological disorders in his *Book for al-Manṣūr*, whereas he uses a much more limited drug range and more simple treatments in his *Book of experiences*. This is not, in and of itself, very surprising, as even nowadays general practitioners often resort to the same tried and tested remedies (eg paracetamol, aspirin, antibiotics), whereas the *Merck manual* records many more therapeutical options than the average GP would ever use.

Al-Rāzī wrote many more medical works, some on individual topics such as sexual hygiene (Pormann 2007b), individual medicinal substances such as oxymel, or the question of why we sometimes undress to get warmer.

For me, al-Rāzī symbolises like no other the fruitful engagement with the previous medical tradition, as well as the innovation that partly becomes possible because of the new institutional set-up. Take the genre of the case histories as an example. Al-Rāzī insists that the Hippocratic *Epidemics* are models that one ought to follow (Pormann 2008c: 107–8). But it was only the hospital environment that made certain progress possible. Al-Rāzī reports in his *Doubts about*

Galen that he observed 'two thousand patients' suffering from dropsy; and he presumably recorded the success or failure of certain treatments, as he refers to statistical data in this passage. This large number of cases allows al-Rāzī to develop a new treatment (Pormann 2008c: 108–9). In other words, al-Rāzī is inspired to take careful case notes by a Greek text, the Hippocratic *Epidemics*. The *Epidemics*, however, do not contain records of a statistical nature. It is only the institution of the hospital that allows al-Rāzī to observe a sufficient number of cases to draw his conclusions (Pormann 2013c). The institution of the hospital enjoyed legal security in Islamic law, and continued a tradition of charity that was undoubtedly at least partly inspired by earlier Christian models. But an elite practitioner like al-Rāzī was firmly engaged in hospital practice, and he could further that practice through this institution.

Al-Rāzī also excelled in alchemy and wrote about occult properties (Ullmann 1972: 210–13, 407). For instance, in the introduction to his *On the hidden properties of things* (*Fī Ḫawāṣṣ al-ašyāʾ*), al-Rāzī insists that one should not merely reject the topic of hidden properties because some people do not believe in them. Rather, evidence is required; and according to al-Rāzī, hidden properties do exist, or at least no persuasive evidence against their existence has been offered. 'For', al-Rāzī says, 'evidence stating that a hidden property is like this or that is not more necessary than the [evidence] stating that a hidden property is *not* like this or that.' (Iskandar 2011: 224) In other words, one cannot positively establish that they never have their hidden effects. His treatise *On the hidden properties of things* then lists some 100 occult properties in alphabetical order, and many of them have medical applications. Today, most physicians would feel uncomfortable about a prominent physician advocating magical practices. But we should not forget that for al-Rāzī, hidden properties represent an area of study that requires the use of evidence, just as medicine does. Finally, one should say that a lot more research is required to show how al-Rāzī's alchemical interests intersect with his medical endeavours. It is hard to imagine that there is no cross-over between the two fields, but in al-Rāzī's writings on medical substances we do not find many alchemical echoes. We are therefore far away from the much later chemical medicine of the Paracelsians (see chapter 7 below). This short excursion into al-Rāzī's magical and alchemical interests should not, however, detract from his great skill as a clinician and medical author.

Further reading

For a first taste of al-Rāzī as clinician, with many primary sources cited, see Iskandar (2011). Pormann (2008c) explores how the institutional context of the Islamic hospital was important for al-Rāzī to develop new treatments and to test them. He (2007b) also investigates how al-Rāzī's approach to a given topic can vary according to genre, taking sexual intercourse as an example. Pauline Koetschet (2011) discusses al-Rāzī's attitude to melancholy, and this work contains many fascinating insights into the interrelationship between philosophy and medicine. Peter Adamson's book (in preparation) promises to be the authoritative work on al-Rāzī's philosophy, but also touches on the relationship between medicine and philosophy. In the meantime, Daiber (2012), offers an overview of al-Rāzī's philosophical œuvre.

Exhibition items

> No 12 (MSTR30): composite late 15th-century manuscript containing al-Rāzī's *Curing within the hour*

Al-Rāzī's treatise on *Curing within the hour* is fairly short, consisting of 25 very concise chapters on various ailments that can be treated within the hour. The manuscript displayed here comprises two texts. In its first and much longer part, it contains an *Abridgment of the 'aide-mémoire'* (*Kitāb Muḫtaṣar al-taḏkira*), that is the abridged version by the Ṣūfī theologian and mystic ʿAbd al-Wahhāb al-Šaʿrānī (or al-Šaʿrāwī; d 1565) of the *Aide-mémoire* by the physician al-Suwaydī (1204–92). The second part only occupies two leaves (67–8), and contains Al-Rāzī's *Curing within the hour*; it does not, however, contain the whole treatise, but only the beginning of the treatise on fol 67 and the end on fol 68. There must have been at least one, possibly more, additional quires containing the rest of the text. We therefore have here only a fragment (**Fig 4.2**).

This fragment, however, is interesting in that it contains the introduction to *Curing within the hour*, in which al-Rāzī explains why and how he came to write it. One day at court, a discussion erupted around a medical topic, and someone present stated that 'diseases are caused by substances that have accumulated over the course of days and month. What has been constituted in this way can hardly be cured within an hour. It rather requires days and months to cure the patient'. But al-Rāzī informed the ruler that there are, in fact, some diseases and discomforts that can be removed within the hour. The ruler then enjoined al-Rāzī to compose a treatise on this topic, and al-Rāzī complied, the result being his *Curing within the hour*. This said, al-Rāzī makes it plain that there are many diseases that cannot be cured within the hour (one might say, most, as he only lists a few). Quickly curable diseases include certain types of headaches and migraines, for instance, or toothache and halitosis. Take the example of tinnitus. Al-Rāzī says very briefly here: 'It is treated by soaking excellent opium in water and dripping it into the ear, for it will subside immediately.'

Our manuscript also contains the end of the treatise with the final, 25th, chapter. It deals with a tingling sensation that you get when you wash your hands in the winter in cold water. Here, the solution is fairly straightforward: put the hands of the patient into warm salty water.

The last page also contains a colophon, that is, a note by the scribe in which he explains how and when he finished the manuscript. Such colophons are important indicators about manuscript productions, and especially dating. In the present case, the scribe stated in the colophon that 'he finished this blessed book through God's generous kindness and bounteous graciousness at the end of Thursday, 24 of the month Muḥarram in the year 898 (ie 15 November 1492)'. We therefore have the exact date here.

> No 13 (MSTR41): composite medieval manuscript containing a Persian translation of al-Rāzī's *Curing within the hour*

This manuscript contains 10 different Persian medical treatises, ranging in topic from venesection (items 4–5; see **no 21**), poisons and antidotes (item 3), to materia medica (items 1, 9, 10) and diarrhoea (item 2), and to general medicine (item 8), ophthalmology (item 7) and finally *Curing within the hour* (item 6).

The Persian translator of this text writes a very Arabised Persian. For instance, the chapter headings and some of the subheadings, such as 'ʿ*ilāǧ*' (the treatment), remain in Arabic. Likewise, many of the ingredients in the recipes are nearly the same in Arabic and in Persian. This ambiguity raises the question of language and linguistic belonging.

Sometimes, the term 'Arabic' has been used here as a short form for 'Arabic-writing' or 'Arabic-

واندروماس وابن افسطموس وارسطوماحس والخليل
بن احمد والحافظ والبدر القلانسي وبرنفوس وبواص وبوعلاوس
وفرعامس وسطوالس وسعطوس وسندنوس وسندرمس
وسقراطيس وشمويل وعبد الله بن حاربل وفقراطيس وفو
فورس وغاليوس وسفرطس واوطور واراطوس وكسرى
ووطراطس وهرمس واطال في ذلك في الاصل وفي هذا القدر
كفايه في طمانينه القلب الى استعمال ما فيه من الادويه فالله تعالى
سفح به المسلمين بجاه محمد افضل الخلق اجمعين وحسبنا الله
ونعم الوكيل ولا حول ولا قوه الا بالله العلي العظيم

كتاب برو ساعه

بسم الله الرحمن الرحيم وبه نستعين

اما بعد حمد لله مستحق الحمد كما هو اهله والصلاه والسلام
على سيدنا محمد خاتم انبيايه ورسله فيقول ابو بكر محمد بن
زكريا الرازي رحمه الله تعالى كنت عند الوزير ابن القسم بن
عبد الله يوما فجرى بحضرته ذكر شي من الطب وبالمجلس
جماعه ممن يدعيه فتكلم كل واحد منهم في ذلك بمقدار ما
بلغه علمه حتى قال بعضهم ان العلل تتكون من مواد قد اجتمعت
في مرور الليالي والايام والشهور والاعوام فهذا سبيل كونه
لا يبرا في ساعه وتتداوى في مثل ذلك من الايام والشهور حتى يتم
العليل في الاخر فتسمع ذلك جماعه ممن حضر من المتطببين
كل ذلك يريدون المجي والذهاب الى العليل واخذ الشي فعرفت
الوزيران من العلل ما يجتمع في ايام ويبرا في ساعه فتعجبوا من
من ذلك فسالني الوزيران اولف كتابا يشتمل على جميع العلل
التي تبرا في ساعه فبادرت الى منزلي والفت هذا الكتاب
واجتهدت فيه وجعلته كما هو سيانات في تاليف الكتب
من الفرق الى القدم وذكرت العلل التي يجوز ان يبدا ويبري
او تبرا في ساعه واحده فلا جل ذلك ذكرت اعضا وتركت اعضا
كثيره وهذا الكتاب هو دستور الطب وسميته كتاب برو ساعه

speaking' author. Take al-Rāzī as an example. His name indicates that he came from the city of Rayy, now a suburb of modern Teheran. We also know that he spent significant amounts of time there, for instance as hospital director. Therefore, his mother tongue, or at least the vernacular language with which he had constant contact, must have been Persian. And yet, all the works by him of which we know were written in Arabic. For al-Rāzī, therefore, there seems not to have been any hesitation in writing in this language. By the second half of the 9th century, it had certainly established itself as the *lingua franca* of medicine, science, philosophy, but also poetry and literature more generally. Yet this dominant position was challenged by the so-called '*šuᶜūbīya*' or 'popularism' movement, which reaffirmed ethnic and linguistic identities other than that of the Arabs.

Not surprisingly, then, when Avicenna (Ibn Sīnā) wrote roughly a century after al-Rāzī, he did author at least some of his works in Persian, most famously his *Däneš-nāma* (or 'Book of knowledge'); this is a Persian philosophical encyclopaedia, and perhaps the first attempt to render peripatetic philosophy systematically in this language. And yet, when dealing with medicine, Avicenna appears to have used Arabic exclusively, although later Persian authors translated him into this language.

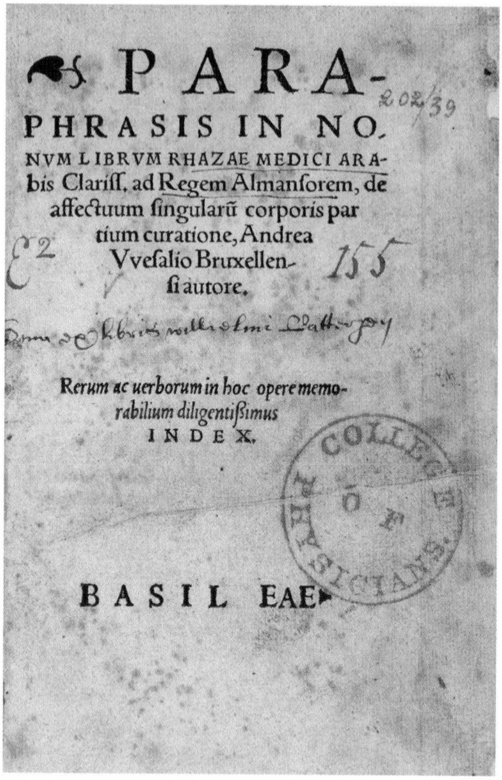
PARAPHRASIS IN NONVM LIBRVM RHAZAE MEDICI ARAbis Clariss. ad Regem Almansorem, de affectuum singularū corporis partium curatione, Andrea Vvesalio Bruxellensi autore.

Rerum ac uerborum in hoc opere memorabilium diligentissimus INDEX.

BASILEAE

Fig 4.3, no 14 *Paraphrasis in Nonum librum Rhazae*, Vesalius, 1537.

No 14 (D2/78-b-25): Vesalius' *Abridgment of the ninth book for Al-Manṣūr*

This item contains an early work by the famous Flemish anatomist Vesalius (1514–64). He achieved international renown with his *Fabric of the human body* (*De humani corporis fabrica*), first published in 1543, and issued in a second edition in 1555; moreover, Vesalius continued to work on this book with a view to preparing a third edition, although it never appeared (Nutton 2012). He wrote the *Abridgment of the 'ninth book' by al-Rāzī, the most famous Arab physician, for King al-Manṣūr on how to treat the affections of the individual parts of the body* (*Paraphrasis in nonum librum Rhazae Medici Arabis clarissimi ad Regem Almansorem de singularum corporis partium affectuum curatione*) in 1537, shortly before he finished studying medicine. The *Ninth book for al-Manṣūr* is part of al-Rāzī's medical encyclopaedia called *Book for al-Manṣūr* in 10 books. Book nine deals with so-called topical diseases, that is, diseases affecting a particular part of the body. As such, it proved very popular in the Latin West (see **no 15**).

Vesalius' *Abridgment* illustrates well the attitude of Renaissance physicians towards Arabic learning. In the preface, Vesalius talks about his motivation to compose the *Abridgment*. He knows that Greek authorities are superior, but when he looks at current medical practice, he realises that physicians often adopt 'a method that varies from that of the most learned Greeks and constantly (to tell the truth) follows the Arab barbarians assiduously' (*rationem, tantum a Graecorum, doctissimorum hominum modo euariatam, ac barbarorum, Arabumque perpetuo (prope dixerim) uestigiis tam pertinaciter inhaerentem*) (p2). Vesalius draws a twofold conclusion from this: it is necessary to use Arab authors, especially when their doctrines agree with those of the Greeks; and one ought to improve the language in which the ideas of the Arabs are expressed.

Both points are revealing. In the 1530s, most medicine taught at university would have been based on Arabic authors in Latin translation; and Vesalius himself refers to his teachers in Paris who enjoined their students to compare Arabic medical texts (in Latin translation) with Greek sources (again probably in Latin translation) (p3). But like Linacre and Caius, Vesalius also adhered to a stylistic ideal of classical Latin. He described the language of the *Ninth book*'s Latin version as 'this prose style and character which is horrible and uncivilised, just like the general style of the Arabs, so that it does not agree at all with the succinct and elegant prose of the Greeks' (*ipse dictionis stylus et character, adeo horridus et incultus, quemadmodum est Arabum uniuersus, ut nihil omnino cum Graecorum illi concinnitate et elegantia conueniat*) (p3). In other words, Vesalius wanted to purge the Latin prose style of al-Rāzī's text in order to make it more acceptable to his contemporaries.

Therefore, this item shows both the dominance of 'Arab' authors in medical education and practice in the 16h century, but also the threats to which the Arabo-Islamic heritage was exposed.

› No 15 SR5a(7): An early printed version of a Latin commentary on al-Rāzī's *Ninth book for al-Manṣūr*

This item is a so-called incunable, that is, a book printed before 1500. It contains the commentary on al-Rāzī's ninth book for al-Manṣūr by a certain Silano de Nigris from Pavia in northern Italy, about whom little is known. Silano clearly was animated by a strong scholasticism: he explained al-Rāzī's text through constant references to Aristotle. For instance, he referred to Aristotle's *Physics* when explaining why he wrote this commentary; and he lists the four Aristotlian causes – formal, effective, material, final – that compelled him to do so.

In writing his medical handbook called *Book for al-Manṣūr*, al-Rāzī drew heavily on Greek models, and notably the encyclopaedia by Paul of Aegina, as we have already mentioned. It consists of 10 *maqālas* or books, dealing with the following topics: (1) anatomy and physiology; (2) semiotics; (3) simple drugs; (4) regimen; (5) skin diseases and cosmetics; (6) provisions for travellers; (7) surgery; (8) poisons; (9) topical diseases; and (10) fevers. The book on topical diseases – that is, diseases affecting a particular part of the body – is arranged from tip to toe: it starts with headaches and migraines, and dizziness and vertigo, and ends with pains in the extremities. This book proved particularly popular in the West, and it was printed and commented on many times in Latin translation during the Renaissance.

The Latin translation of book nine, as well as of the other books, is due to the efforts of Gerard of Cremona (d 1187), who also translated the *Canon of medicine* (see **no 8**). Gerard, as his name suggests, came from the city of Cremona in northern Italy, but he spent most of his life in Toledo, where he learnt Arabic in order to read works on various topics such astrology and medicine. Toledo was, of course, a major centre of cultural contact at the time; it had come under Christian rule in 1085, but had a very sizeable Muslim and Jewish population who spoke Arabic. Gerard of Cremona therefore represents the translation effort from Arabic into Latin that took place in what used to be Muslim Spain or 'Al-Andalus'.

There had, however, been an earlier wave of medical texts being translated from Arabic into Latin. Its prime mover was Constantine, the African (d before 1099). Constantine came from Ifrīqīya (roughly what is modern Tunisia), and joined the monastery of Monte Casino, but also had ties to the medical school of Salerno. Constantine translated many shorter medical works, especially those by authors linked to Ifrīqīya, such as Isḥāq ibn ʿImrān and Ibn al-Ǧazzār. In the case of the former, he translated Isḥāq's treatise *On melancholy* into Latin, but without any acknowledgement that he was merely the translator, not the author of this text (Omrani 2010). The third centre of Arabo-Latin translation was in Antioch, which lay at the crossroads of various cultures, and which saw a large influx of Latin writers as a result of the Crusades. Here Stephen of Antioch composed not only a trilingual glossary of drug names (in Arabic, Greek and Latin), but also worked on the translation of the *Complete book of the medical art* (*Kāmil al-Ṣināʿa al-ṭibbīya*), also known as the *Royal book* (*Liber Regius*, *al-Kitāb al-Malakī*) by al-Maǧūsī (fl 983) (Burnett 2000).

The incunable on display here therefore illustrates that many Arabic medical texts became available in Latin through translation, and that these Latin versions were often commented on. One should stress, though, that they led to a revolution in medical teaching and practice. In Italy, for instance, the medical school of the Methodists had still quite a few followers, and humoral pathology had not yet won the day by the 10th century. All this was to change with the influx of Arabo-Latin medical texts. In the nascent European universities, most teachers taught medicine through Arabic authors in Latin translation. Not surprisingly then, most of the textbooks that became core curriculum, such as the *Introduction to medicine* (*al-Mudḫal fī l-ṭibb*, *Isagoge Ioannitii*) by Ḥunayn ibn Isḥāq, were of Arabic origin.

> No 16 (D2/94-e-20): Channing's edition and Latin translation of al-Rāzī's *On smallpox and measles*

Al-Rāzī's treatise *On smallpox and measles* (*Fī l-ǧudarī wa-l-ḥaṣba*) is rightly famous. It distinguishes between two conditions that Greek physicians conflated; it therefore represents an important example of medical progress in the area of differential diagnosis. But it is also fascinating for the long history of its transmission into 'Western' languages, being first translated from Arabic into Syriac (the Syriac version is now lost), then from Syriac into Greek and finally from Greek into Latin. The medieval Greek and Latin versions were printed repeatedly during the Renaissance.

Fig 4.4, no 16 *Rhazes de variolis et morbillis, Arabice et Latine*, Channing, 1766.

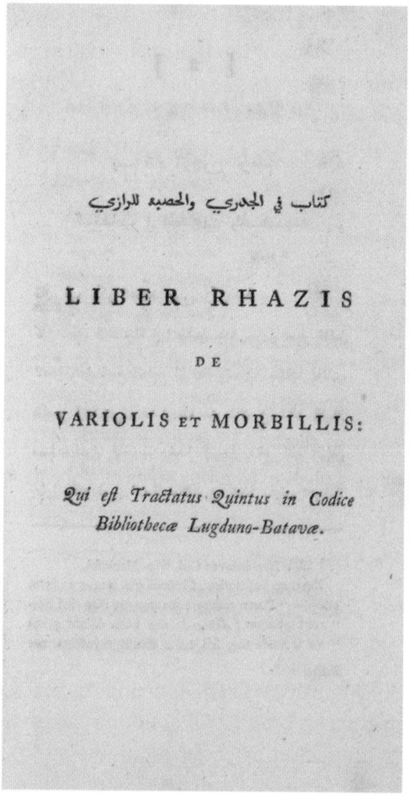
كتاب في الجدري والحصبة للرازي

LIBER RHAZIS

DE

VARIOLIS ET MORBILLIS:

Qui est Tractatus Quintus in Codice Bibliothecæ Lugduno-Batavæ.

Moreover, the 18th century saw a flourish of activities surrounding this text. Richard Mead (1673–1754), a fellow of the RCP, published a new Latin translation, produced by the Laudian professor of Arabic and regius professor of Hebrew at Oxford, Thomas Hunt (1694–1775), on the basis of the work by two other translators, John Gagnier (*c*1670–1740), Lord Almoner's professor of Arabic at Oxford, and the Damascene Solomon Negri. Hunt also became acquainted with John Channing (c1703–75), the first editor of the Arabic text.

His edition was printed in London by Bowyer in 1766, and was accompanied by yet another fresh translation into Latin (see Savage-Smith 1988). John Channing exemplifies the importance of amateur scholarship and learning in the scientific Enlightenment. For Channing worked as an apothecary in London: he was apprentice to his father (1718–26), then worked as a freeman (from 1726 onwards), and rose to occupy high offices within the Worshipful Society of Apothecaries, namely those of renter warden (1770), upper warden (1770) and master (1771). Despite a busy and successful professional life in London, it would appear that he found the time to teach himself not only Greek, but also Hebrew, Persian and Arabic; in this, he resembles his contemporary Henry Wild (1684–1734), the 'Arabian tailor', who learned seven languages in as many years by himself (see below, pp73–4). Thomas Hunt, mentioned above, facilitated Channing's gaining admittance to the Bodleian Library at Oxford, where he studied Arabic and Hebrew manuscripts from 1759 until the year of his death in 1775.

Channing's edition and Latin translation of al-Rāzī's *On smallpox and measles* is among the earliest medical Arabic texts printed in Arabic in the British Isles. Channing's second edition, that of al-Zahrāwī's *Surgery*, printed in Oxford in 1778, constitutes an even greater achievement, and remained the authoritative text for 200 years. Yet Channing's edition of *On smallpox and measles* illustrates al-Rāzī's influence as a clinician more clearly than any other work. Channing's Latin version was quickly translated into French by Paulet, with a view to dealing with epidemiological problems of his day; in other words, it was deemed useful to contemporary medical practice, rather than interesting in historical terms.

William Greenhill, whom we earlier encountered as being interested in translating the Arabic version of the lost parts of Galen's *Anatomical procedures* (**nos 3–4**), produced his English version on the basis of Channing's edition in 1848.

راس انسان فاذا فعلتم ذلك واردتم شهوة انسان للطعام وعقد بها فاطبخوا فيها ما اردتم فمن اكل منه انعقدت شهواته

منه وذهبت شهوته للطعام سنة وذهاب ذلك ان تسقوه ايها في الاواني الذهب كما لا ينام فهو

المنزلة الثالثة والعشرون وهي من ... سنة وهذه المنزلة ارضية سعيدة مسعودة

نحس اذا نزل القمر بهذه المنزلة اعمل فيها نيرنجات القطعية بين الاكابر والبعيد منهم والعداوة بينهم و

دبر فيه السموم واعقدوا الشهوات النساء واطلقوا انفسكم ونجور هذه المنزلة بابونج بري وثقال

تكون كرها في اسماء الملائكة المقربين الموكلين بهلكستنة وهم فور ال ... ال اشمات ال كتا ال

طار ال قال محال ال ... القطعة بين الاكابر والبعد منهم والعداوة بينهم فاذا اردتم ان توقعوا

بين الاكابر العداوة والبغضاء وتباعدوا بينهم فاصنعوا اثنين بصفر الاصفر لصورتين احدهما من

الرصاص وللاخر من الصفر الاصفر وتكتب على صدر كل واحد اسمه وتنقش على ظهره النحس هذه الاشكال الثلاثة

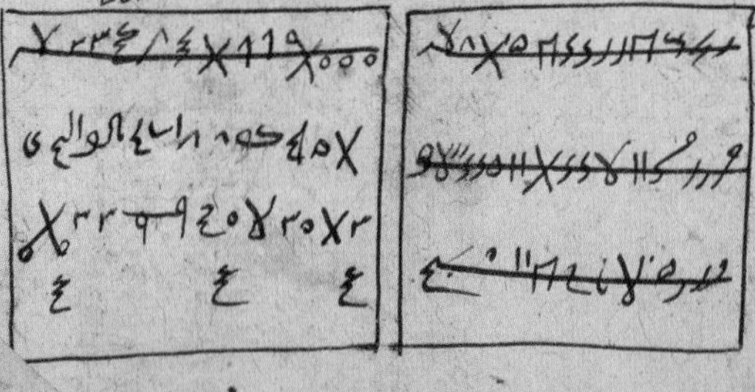

وعلى الظهر

النحس

الرصاص

هذه الاشكال الثلثة

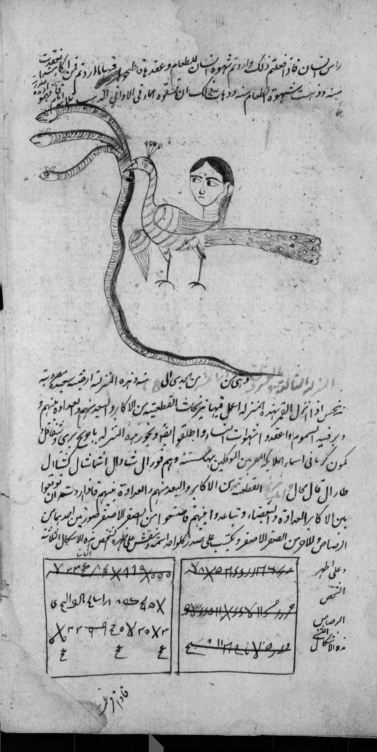

Fig 5.1, no 17 Illustration from a her... s, late 18th century.

إنّا لمّا رأينا لهذه الجواهر أفاعيل كثيرة نافعة لا تبلغ عقولنا معرفة سببها الفاعل ولا تحيط به، لم نر أن نطرح كل شيء لا تدركه وتبلغه عقولنا، لأن في ذلك سقوط جل المنافع عنا؛ بل نضيف إلى ذلك ما أدركناه بالتجارب وشهد لنا الناس.

We say that we have observed that these precious stones [ǧawāhir] have many useful actions, yet our intellect is unable to know and grasp their active cause. Therefore, we decided not to omit everything which our intellect cannot understand or know, since this would imply that we forego many benefits. Rather, we add to this what we know from experience or to which people have testified. (Abū Bakr al-Rāzī in the preface to his *Book on the hidden properties of things* (ed Iskandar 2011: 224–5))

5 Magic, divination and astrology

The Hippocratic treatise *On the sacred disease* is generally considered a manifesto for rational medicine, since its author argues against the notion that epilepsy is a disease sent by the gods. Yet, the author does not pitch science against religion in general, as he clearly believes in the gods and their sacredness. Therefore, he states at the end of his work that:

> this disease, which is called sacred, is brought about by the same causes as the other diseases, namely by things that come to, and depart from [the body], such as cold, the sun, and winds, which constantly change and never keep still. These are godly things, so that one does not need to make a distinction and consider the disease [epilepsy] more godly than the other diseases; rather, everything is divine and everything human.

In other words, the author does not deny the influence of the gods: they pervade everything and are ultimately responsible for maintaining nature's order, but he does argue against those who claim that epilepsy in particular is a 'sacred disease', caused by the gods. Likewise, most medical authors in the medieval period did not adopt an atheist position. Rather, they saw Nature (with a capital N) as being sustained by divine will; to comprehend Nature's laws was to understand divine providence, as the example of anatomy, discussed above (p29), also makes clear.

In a world in which the supernatural played a significant role, it is not surprising to find many people routinely appealing to supernatural forces in order to avert or confront disease. This is true for the Christian Middle Ages as it is for the medieval Islamic world. It therefore comes as no surprise that the great scientist, clinician and philosopher al-Rāzī also defended the study of magic vigorously as something based on evidence (*burhān*) and experience (*taǧriba*) (see above, p43 and the opening quotation). In the following, I shall briefly review four areas of what one would nowadays consider 'pseudo-science' that formed an important part of man's response to ailments and adversities in the Middle Ages and beyond; these are hermeticism, astrology, divination and magic through the use of bowls and talismans.

The figure of Hermes Trismegistus ('thrice great') and texts attributed to him played a significant role in the Arabic tradition (van Bladel 2009). On the one hand, there are the many legends about this Hermes, linked to the Egyptian god Toth, who wrote on the secrets of creation. He is linked to certain astrological books, to writings about talismans and amulets, to treatises on poison, and he appears in the so-called gnomological literature, that is, the literature recording the wise and pithy sayings of various philosophers. Hermes' link to alchemy is particularly strong, and many works on this topic are either attributed to Hermes as the mystical author or claim to contain some of his knowledge on the topic. Many of the Hermetic texts in Arabic have Greek antecedents, sometimes transmitted via Middle Persian (or Pahlavi).

Astrology and astronomy were intimately intertwined in classical and medieval times. The greatest Greek authority on astronomy, Claudius Ptolemy, for instance, is also one of the foremost authorities on astrology. He not only wrote works mostly concerned with what one would nowadays call astronomical questions, such as his *Almagest* (*Ἡ μεγίστη σύνταξις*), *Handy tables* (*Πρόχειροι κανόνες*) and *Planetary hypotheses* (*Ὑποθέσεις τῶν πλανωμένων*), but also the most influential astrological work, the *Tetrábiblos* (known in Latin as *Quadripartitum*). All these texts were translated into Arabic as well, and enjoyed great popularity throughout the medieval period, although various Islamic astronomers challenged a number of Ptolemy's models (Saliba 2007). Moreover, some astronomers and theologians tried to separate the discipline of mathematical astronomy from that of astrology, which they criticised (Saliba 1994, 53–61, 66–72).

In medicine, Galen had also advocated that one should pay heed to the stars, following Hippocrates' opinion 'that astronomy contributes not very little, but rather very much to medicine' (ὅτι οὐκ ἐλάχιστον μέρος ξυμβάλλεται ἀστρονομίη ἐς ἰητρικὴν, ἀλλὰ πάνυ πλεῖστον) (*Airs, waters, places* i 2; ed Littré 1839–61, ii 14). Galen discussed the influence of the stars in particular in his work on *Critical days*. It was translated into Arabic, and other authors such as al-Kindī (d *c*866) and Qusṭā ibn Lūqā (d *c*912) also wrote on this topic (Cooper 2011). A typical argument about why the position of the stars matters to one's health is presented by Abū Maᶜšar (d 886) in his *Great introduction* (ed Klein-Franke 1984: 110):

> Physicians know about the dominance of heat or cold and moist or dry that occurs in the human body at [different] seasons. Intelligent scholars, however, predict the types of diseases, fevers, and swellings that occur in the living body; how each disease and ailment differs in strength and weakness; whether it is increasing or decreasing; how long it will last or how quickly it will cease; and whether the patient will recover or not. They make these predictions on the basis of what they observe, such as the difference in the air of the land, the age of the living being, and the fact that one nature dominates the body. They say that one can deduce these things from the mixture of the year, the difference in the air – whether it is healthy or unhealthy – the change of time, and the alteration of the nature. Through these things, physicians deduce how the natures change with the seasons and the air of the country. The change of the natures, however, is only brought about by the movement of the stars, because the sun has the power to heat, whereas the moon has the power to moisten. This is evident from the effects that the stars have when they mix with the sun and the moon during each season.

Abū Maᶜšar thus says that environmental factors

clearly influence health, and that the environment is influenced by the stars. This fundamental point is easily taken: after all, there would be no life on earth without the sun and its power to warm us. The influence of the Moon, too, is clearly visible in the tides and other phenomena.

Therefore, we find astrological elements in medieval medical writings (Akasoy *et al* 2008). One author, Yuḥannā ibn Ṣalt (fl 870-910), who was acquainted with Ḥunayn ibn Isḥāq, even wrote a *Compendium on astrological medicine* (*Kunnāš ṭibbī nuǧūmī*), comprising 10 chapters dealing with topics such as zodiac signs, the special quality of stars, how to pick the right time to take drugs or let blood, and so on.

Prognosis, the faculty to predict the future course of a disease, is an important skill for any physician. This topic is discussed in the Hippocratic Corpus and by Galen, as well as by many later Arabic-speaking authors, as we have seen (see p5 above). It is also a widely acceptable technique today, provided that it is based on the physiology of the patient and other physical factors. Yet, in the medieval world, other means of prognosis were also employed that fall within the remit of divination. Astrology played a great role here, as did divination by reading palms (*ʿilm al-asārīr*, 'chiromancy'), observing the flight of birds (*ṭiyara*), looking at patterns in the sand (*ʿilm al-raml*, 'geomancy') or even interpreting the patient's name (*ʿilm al-ḥurūf*, 'onomancy').

In the medieval Islamic world, magical practices were often mixed with religious devotion. For instance, magic-medicinal bowls (such as **no 19**) combine magic and religious devotion (Maddison, Savage-Smith 1997: i, 72–105). On some of these bowls, verses from the Koran are inscribed, such as the *Throne verse* (*Āyat al-Kursī*, 2: 255), or the last three short *sūras*, called *Devotion* (*al-Iḫlāṣ*, 112), *Firmament* (*al-Falaq*, 113) and *People* (*al-Nās*, 114), all of which are highly memorable through their use of rhyme and alliteration. But they also sometimes contain magical squares or other magical symbols. From the inscriptions on bowls, we can often glean their medicinal uses, such as curing intestinal disorders, headaches, fevers and so on. Although more than 100 such magical-medicinal bowls from the 9th to the 19th survive, they are rarely mentioned in the medical literature. A 14th-century manual on *Prophetic medicine* recommends that one should drink water before breakfast from a bowl inscribed with verses of the Koran and magical squares; this serves as a prophylactic measure against melancholy and delusion. And a medical manuscript from the 13th century suggests inscribing a magical formula on a bowl (or a plate) and drinking from it.

Drinking water that has come into contact with magical or Koranic texts is only one way in which the written word could be put to use against disease. Another was the carrying of talismans. A talisman, Arabic *ṭilsām* from the Greek *télesma* (lit 'ritual'), often took the form of a pendant in which one enclosed a piece of writing that would ward off disease. Interestingly, both manuals on how to write talismans and the objects themselves have come down to us from the medieval period. For instance, the 13th-century author al-Būnī (d 1225) wrote a manual with the title *Great sun of knowledge* (*Šams al-Maʿrifa al-Kubrā*), in which he gives detailed instructions on how to write talismans. Suprisingly, however, the objects that were actually used do not follow the guidelines given by al-Būnī and others in the theoretical literature. Therefore, it would appear that we have a discrepancy between the theory of magic as contained in the written works on the topic and its practice as reflected in the objects themselves.

Further reading

An up-to-date overview of magic and divination can be found in Savage-Smith (2004), with a focus on the early material. Maddison and Savage-Smith (1997) is lavishly illustrated and contains very detailed and pertinent discussions of both texts and objects. Finally, Savage-Smith (2011: 761–789) lists many prominent texts and discusses them in detail. On medicine and astrology, see Akasoy *et al* (2008).

Exhibition items

> No 17 (MSTR42): A late 18th-century manuscript, containing two Hermetic texts

In the Arabic tradition, we find a series of texts attributed to certain strange personages with names such as al-Hādīṭūs or al-Mīyālāṭīs and dealing with writing talismans and other magical objects. Kevin van Bladel (2004: 322; cf 2009: 184) has labelled these texts 'talismanic pseudo-Aristotelian Hermetica'. The names of their presumed authors have been made up, probably to sound Greek, but they are not actually translations of Greek texts. In the present manuscript, we find two texts, and the first on fols 1–24 belongs to this group of talismanic pseudo-Aristotelian Hermetica. From the colophon on fol 24b, we know that it is 'the book called *Mīyāṭālāyis* in Greek, the praiser of God, who created the active intellect and caused perfect knowledge to emanate'. There is no Greek equivalent to the title *Mīyāṭālāyis*; this suggests that it was invented to lend the text greater authority through its presumed Greek origin. The text itself deals with astrological phenomena such as the lunar mansions, and spells and charms are sprinkled in throughout. Moreover, there are numerous illustrations in this text, such as the one on fol 21b (**Fig 5.1**). It shows a woman (visible only as a head) looking onto a scene in which a pheasant holds a three-headed serpent in its beak.

The second text is a *Book on the occult properties and uses of stones, the talismans that one carves on them, and other uses and noble occult properties* (*Kitāb Ḫawāṣṣ al-aḥǧār wa-manāfiʿihā wa-mā yunqašu ʿalayhā min al-ṭilasmāt wa-ġayr ḏālika min al-manāfiʿ wa-l-ḫawāṣṣ al-šarīfa*) by the secretary (*al-kātib*) or mathematician (*al-ḥāsib*) ʿUṭārid ibn Muḥammad. Little is known about this author, who probably lived in the 9th century and also wrote several works on astronomy and astrology. In the preface to this book on stones, ʿUṭārid explains why he wrote it. He had perused numerous other Hermetic texts on the subject and found much ambiguity in them. Therefore, he decided to pen a work that would be clear and contained all the necessary information about the subject. In the book, ʿUṭārid links the subjects of stones and their occult properties to that of astrology. There is a section in which various stones are linked to the planets. On fol 26b, for instance, the stones associated with Mars (*al-Mirrīḫ*) are mentioned; and on fol 27b, those with Venus (*al-Zuhara*).

> No 18 (MS353): A Renaissance manuscript that contains the horoscope for a certain John, born on 12 April 1538 at 9.39pm, as well as interpretative and explanatory texts and tables

To understand the rationale behind this horoscope, one has first to come to grips with the basic cosmology to which most medieval thinkers adhered, and which is largely based on Aristotle's *On the heaven* (known in Latin as *De caelo*) and refined by Claudius Ptolemy. According to this cosmology, the earth is at the centre of the universe (or the cosmos). Above it we find concentric spheres on which the planets move. The word 'planet' here includes the Moon, Mercury, Venus, Sun, Mars, Jupiter and Saturn: that is, celestial bodies that we would no longer classify as planets but rather as moons (the Moon) and fixed stars (the Sun). Above these runs the sphere of the fixed stars. We all live in the world underneath the sphere of the Moon, the so-called sublunar world. This is the world of coming-to-be and passing-away, of generation and corruption, where the four elements (earth, air, fire, water) constantly change. In the world above the Moon, the planets and stars are made of the fifth element or 'quintessence', and subject neither to generation nor to corruption. The circular motion of the spheres is perfect, and it affects the fates and fortunes of those living in the sublunar world.

When casting a horoscope, the astrologer has to determine the position of the fixed stars moving on the outer sphere, as well as that of the planets. He calculates the ascendant, the 'point of the ecliptic, or degree of the zodiac, which...is just rising above the eastern horizon' (*Oxford English dictionary*). Then he determines what zodiac sign is in the house of the ascendant, and whether it has a 'lord', that is one or more planets that are within the house. These basic principles of what is called judicial astrology (*ʿilm aḥkām al-nuǧūm*, literally 'the science of stars' judgements' in Arabic) are shared between the Arabic and the Latin traditions.

It should be stressed, however, that not everybody accepted astrology as a valid science. Take the example of Avicenna: he wrote an *Epistle on the refutation of astrology* (*Risāla fī Ibṭāl ʿilm aḥkām al-nuǧūm*; Michot 2006), in which he attacked the predictions of astrologers. He talked specifically about medicine, arguing that although medicine and astrology both belong to the branches of knowledge that are prone to error (see above, p22), medicine is based on better principles than astrology. For instance, the physician examines the pulse and breathing to diagnose disease, whereas the astrologer does none of these things. To be sure, Avicenna mistrusted the prediction of astrologers. He did not, however, doubt that the movement of the spheres influenced life on earth; he simply believed that the exact effect of this influence remains unknown and probably also unknowable.

Despite the criticism of some people, astrology remained popular throughout the Middle Ages, and continued to be practised during the Renaissance, as the present manuscript shows. At its centre, between fols 10 and 12, we find an 'astronomical circle containing the places and aspects of the planets and the fixed stars at a 2°20' elevation of the pole' (*circulus astronomicus Continens loca et aspectus planetarum et stellas fixas principales. Elev*[*atione*]*. Poli. 2.20*). The legend reads 'On 12 April 1538 at 9h39 pm John was born in London through verified conception' (*1538. 12. Aprillis hora 9 mi.39 post meridiem natus in Londino Johannes per conceptionem verificatam*). We therefore know that the horoscope was cast for one John from London, but nothing else is known about him. The beginning of the manuscript (fols 1–5) contains astrological tables from 1538–1609, so that 1609 is probably the year in which the manuscript was produced. On fols 6–10 follows a short treatise 'On the natures and properties of the seven planets' (*De natura et proprietatibus septem planetarum*). The rest of the manuscript contains further texts connected to this horoscope, which end with the sentence: 'From the things written above you will be able to deduce whatever will happen in any given year because of the instruction of the stars' (*Ex prescriptis colligere potes quid quolibet anno contingere poterit ex instructu* [?] *astrorum*).

> No 19 (Object number A639330): Small brass magical-medicinal bowl, probably a 19th-century copy of a 13th-century original of Syro-Egyptian origin; unsigned

This bowl is probably a late copy of an earlier one that belongs to a group of so-called poison cups. This name derives from the fact that the inscriptions indicate that drinking from it helps – among other things – against the poisons of scorpions and serpents. The inscription here reads (tr E Savage-Smith, slightly modified):

> This blessed cup neutralises all poisons. In it have been gathered proven benefits...It is useful for the bite of serpent and scorpion and fever, for a woman in labour and increasing milk, for [the bite of] a rabid dog, for abdominal pain and colic, for migraine and throbbing pain, for hepatic and splenic fever, for [increasing] strength, for [stopping] haemorrhage, and for all diseases and afflictions. The afflicted person or his agent should drink from it, and then they will be cured, through the help of God.

It may well have been dedicated to the Mamluk Sultan of Egypt al-Malik al-Muʿizz ʿIzz al-Dunyā wa-l-Dīn Aybak (d 1257), and is similar to a poison cup now part of the Khalili collection (Maddison, Savage-Smith 1997: i 73 and note 15).

واحد ثلثة دراهم يدق الجميع وينخل ويعجن ببياض البيض ويطلى به الوجه ويغسل بماء النخالة **غوشنة**
نوع من الكمأة يجفف فينتفخ ويصير شكله كشكل كاس صغير يغسل به الثياب ويؤكل في الحموضات وهو بارد
رطب في الدرجة الاولى وليس في برد الكمأة وليس بردي الخلط كالكمأة **باب الفاء** **فانيذ** اجوده الابيض
المعمول من السكر نقي وهو اغلظ من السكر وهو حار رطب في الاولى وقيل ان حرارته في الثالثة والسجزي منه حار رطب
في الثانية وهو ينفع من السعال ويلين البطن ويولد دما معتدلا وهو جيد للصدر وصنعته ان يحل السكر بماء
يسير ونار هادية ويقعد فاذا ابتدا لا ينعقد ضرب على وتد مسمور ضربا جيدا حتى يبيض فاذا ابتدا بالجفاف
قبل ان يبقى فيقرب وهو في البدء الى النار ليلين ثم يمد على الخشبة فاذا استحكم قطع اقطاعا وترك على طبق حتى
يجف **فالوذج** اجوده السكري وهو حار ينفع الصدر والرئة وهو كثير الغذاء ولكنه بطي الهضم يضر من به
السدد في الطحال او في الكبد ولذلك كان من الاصوب ان يقلل نشاه ويكثر سكره وصنعته سكر جزو او عسل
او منهما وسدس جزو نشا او ثمن جزو يذاف النشا بالماء والزعفران ويصفى ويجعل الى طنجير والاجود ان
يكون يعجن حتى يجتمع فاذا صار جملة واحدة يجعل معه العسل او السكر بعد ان يحل بشي منه وهو حار و
ويجعل عليه الباقي في دفعات ويحرك حتى يجتمع ثم يسقى ربع جزو من الشيرج الطري او دهن اللوز او دهن
الجوز ويحرك حتى يخرج دهنه فاذا اريد رطبا لم يستقص عقده وان اريد معقودا فيستخرج معظم دهنه
بالعقد ثم يخلط معه اللوز ويرفع وان عمل بنشا اللوز مخلوطا بنشا الحنطة كان اوفق **فالوذ**
جيد تغذو كثيرا وتصلح الابدان القوية الجيدة الهضوم وصنعتها ان يقطع اللحم صغارا مستطيلا
مربعا ويعرق ثم يلقى عليه الشيرج الطري ودارصيني ثم يغمر بالماء ويطبخ حتى ينطبخ ويعود الى دهنه ويعيد
موردا اندايا غير محل ثم يلقى عليه السكر مدقوق وعسل محلول طبرزد ويوقد تحته حتى ينعقد ثم يلقى فيه اللوز و
يصبغ بالزعفران وتعطر بماء الورد ومن ارادها اشد انعقادا القى على الرطلين من السكر والعسل اوقية
او اقل من النشا كمر وسا في ما ويعقد واذا غرف زين بالسنبوسج المكلل الابيض **فاشرا** هو
الهزارجشان ويقال هزار رجسان وهو الكرمة البيضا وهو من الاصول وهو حار يابس في الثالثة وهو
حاد حريف يجلو او يلطف ادا اصلح اكرسنه يجلو ظاهر البدن ويبقيه ويذهب بالكلف والآثار السود

ويقطع

Fig 6.1, no 20 *Course of explanation abou*
Minhāǧ al-bayān fī-mā yastaʿmiluhu l-i

وينبغي أن تلزم نفسك شيئين أحدهما أن تنفع
المريض والآخر ألّا تضره

You ought to adhere to two things: first to benefit the patient, and second not to harm him.
(Arabic translation of the Hippocratic *Epidemics* (Madrid, Escorial, MS árabe 804, fol 20a, lines 8–9))

6 Therapeutics through medication, cupping and venesection

Both Galen and Avicenna defined medicine as the art that restores health when absent. To do this, medical practitioners developed a whole arsenal of therapeutic measures, ranging from diet and exercise to medication and surgery. From a modern perspective, some of the measures that were part of former medical practice now seem quaint. One recent book even argued that doctors did more harm than good until the early 20th century (Wootton 2007). But 'not to harm' the patient was a fundamental principle of Hippocratic medicine, a principle that also guided physicians in the medieval Islamic world. Given that the placebo effect influences the therapeutic value of modern treatments significantly, one should not be too quick to judge whether or not an ancient therapy was beneficial or not. In the literature, we often find physicians and other medical practitioners commenting on the positive effect of their therapeutic measures; it is hard to imagine that they all lied or were mistaken. Nor could doctors have risen to great fame as clinicians if they had never succeeded.

Physicians in the medieval Islamic world certainly had a large array of therapies at their disposal. Regimen, diet and exercise undoubtedly occupied a privileged place when doctors endeavoured to prevent and to cure illness. They would adjust the so-called 'six non-naturals', that is, factors external to the 'nature' of the patient. They included: (1) the ambient air; (2) food and drink; (3) sleeping and waking; (4) activity and rest; (5) retention and evacuation; and (6) mental states. The fifth aspect encompasses evacuation through urination, bowel movement and sexual intercourse. The sixth one provides a theoretical framework for what one might call psychological treatments, such as talking to the patients, letting them listen to pleasant music, and so on.

The regulation of the 'nature' of the patient, that is, his or her individual mixture, also played a significant role. Each of the four humours was linked to two of the four primary qualities: dry or wet, and warm or cold. Therefore, an imbalance in the humours also resulted in an imbalance of these primary qualities. In his work on *Simple drugs*, Galen had devised a system of degrees for these primary qualities that he attributed to various medicinal substances (see **no 1**). Medical practitioners in the Arabo-Islamic tradition further developed and completed this system (Pormann 2011b). They wrote works on both simple and compound drugs. One such example is *The course of explanation about what man uses* (*Minhāǧ al-bayān fī-mā yastaʿmiluhu* *l-insān*) by Ibn al-Ǧazla (d 1100; **no 20**). It consists of a first part on compound drugs and a second part listing mostly simple and some compound drugs according to the Arabic alphabet. We have also seen that Avicenna's *Canon* dealt with both simple (book two) and compound drugs (book five), devoting two out of five books to this topic (Paavilainen 2009).

Pharmacology is one of the areas where innovation is particularly obvious. Through trade and travel, many new drugs entered the medical marketplace. It is also the case that few authors could resist the temptation to alter a recipe that they found in the medical literature. We also have a number of pharmacopoeias (or formularies) that are directly connected to hospitals. For instance, the Christian physician and pharmacologist Sābūr ibn Sahl wrote a formulary that was later adapted in the ʿAḍūdī hospital in Baghdad, founded in 982 (Kahl 2009). Likewise, the hospital physician al-Kaskarī (fl 920s) mentions recipes 'in the version of the hospital' (*nusḫat al-bīmāristān*) more than a dozen times. And an analysis of a popular pharmacopoeia entitled *Management of the [apothecary's] shop and regulation of the important matters* (*Minhāǧ al-dukkān wa-dustūr al-aʿyān*) by the Jewish pharmacist al-Kūhīn al-ʿAṭṭār (fl 1260s) shows that he often altered his descriptions of compound drugs according to need and availability (Chipman 2010).

The influx of new drugs through trade and travel can best be illustrated by an example. Already in the 9th century the Syriac-writing Christian author Ibn Sarābiyūn (fl 870s) included new drugs from the Far East in his medical compendium. For instance, he provides the recipe for an 'Indian pill'; the following quotation contains the title with possible uses and the first two (out of 14) ingredients (Pormann 2011b: 511–12):

> An Indian pill made with musk. It helps the stomach, removes the abhorrent stench of the mouth produced by tooth decay, makes the gums [of the teeth] firm, cleanses the brain, makes one desire to have sex, and simulates the appetite for it [sex].
>
> *Urmāl* [a wood] from Qimār and frankincense, of each one pound (*riṭl*)...

Jim Al-Khalili once described this pill as 'toothpaste, viagra and aspirin' in one. Its multipurpose action is somewhat surprising, although one can understand how an absence of halitosis in a partner might increase sexual desire. But the more serious point here is that this Indian pill contains ingredients such as musk that were largely unknown in the ancient Greek world. The Qimār mentioned here corresponds to 'Khmer' (roughly modern Cambodia). So substances are imported from a far distance and incorporated into a pharmacopoeia based on the principles of humoral pathology.

The preparation of compound drugs took many different forms. Book seven of Ibn Sarābiyūn's *Small compendium* dedicated to this topic, for instance, contains chapters on the following types of drugs: collyria, 'holy remedies' (*hierás*, *Iyāraǧs*), purging remedies, electuaries (*ǧawārišns*), confections (*maʿǧūns*), pills, lozenges, lincti, decoctions, drinks, gargling remedies, oils, enemas, dressings, creams, liniments, powders (*ḏarūrāt*), sternutatories, tooth-powders and ophthalmological drugs. Some compound drugs only comprise a few ingredients, but others have more the 50. For instance, there are many versions for the theriac (*tiryāq*, from Greek *thēriakḗ*), a complex compound drug including viper meat and allegedly beneficial against snakebite; and of the *Mithridateios*, named after king Mithridates, who protected himself against poisons by eating small quantities and thus developing an immunity (Totelin 2004). Many of the compound remedies were prepared with a pestle and mortar (eg **no 23**), and then stored in drug jars.

In the case of very long recipes containing many expensive and rare drugs, the question arises to what extent they represented a literary rather than practical tradition: were they really used by practitioners or were they quoted by doctors to impress their prospective patients with the great sophistication and expense that they involved? In the case of ophthalmology, Cristina Álvarez-Millán (2000) has persuasively argued that al-Rāzī lists many more and more complex recipes in his medical encyclopaedia, the *Book for al-Manṣūr* (*al-Kitāb al-Manṣūrī*), than he used in his everyday practice, as we can gauged from his *Book of experiences* (*Kitāb al-Taǧārib*).

Another very popular technique was cupping. The idea behind cupping is to extract disease matter (Arabic *mādda*). During certain processes in the body, waste products such as superfluities (Arabic *fuḍūl*; Greek *perittṓmata*) accumulate and can lead to certain diseases. A number of avenues are open to extract them from the body: the physician can purge the patient through an emetic (ie by inducing vomiting) a laxative (ie by provoking bowel movement) or a diuretic drug (ie by stimulating urination). Cupping, however, was a particularly prized technique. Here one first heats a cupping glass (see **no 22**). The air inside the cupping glass expands. Then the cupping glass is applied to the skin of the patient, so that the rim of the glass forms a seal with the skin. As the cupping glass cools down, the air retracts, and a negative pressure is created. This leads to suction, and the skin is drawn up. The two main types of cupping are dry cupping and wet cupping. In the case of the former, the cupping glass is applied to the skin in the manner just mentioned. The waste products and disease matters are drawn to the surface, although this is not immediately visible. In the case of wet cupping, however, the practitioner scarifies the skin beforehand, that is, he or she makes shallow incisions in the skin to as to draw small amounts of blood.

Bloodletting is a far more drastic procedure, that is also called phlebotomy and venesection – both meaning 'cutting the vein' in Greek and Latin respectively. During this procedure, a particular vein in the body is cut, and blood drawn for a certain amount of time, sometimes until the patient faints. The choice of the vein is partly determined by the ailment from which the patient suffers. For instance, the cephalic vein (*al-qīfāl*) is named as such because it is often bled in case of headache, cephalic meaning 'related to the head' (from Greek *kephalikós*). In Manṣūr's *Anatomy*, these veins, used for bloodletting, are clearly labelled (see **Fig 3.1** on p28). The main veins in the arms, used for phlebotomy, are the basilic vein (*basīlīq*), the cephalic vein (*qīfāl*), and the median vein (*al-akhal*). The saphenous vein in the foot is also labelled (*al-ʿirq al-sāfin*) there.

Exhibition items

› No 20 (MSTR25): A late 17th-century manuscript containing Ibn Ǧazla's manual on simple and compound drugs

Ibn Ǧazla (d 1100) is famous for writing two works, the *Course of explanation about what man uses* (*Minhāǧ al-bayān fī-mā yastaʿmiluhu l-insān*), contained in the present manuscript; and the *Almanac of bodily parts for the treatment of people* (*Taqwīm al-abdān fī tadbīr al-insān*). The latter is a manual in which the author organised information about diseases in the form of tables. In each case, he listed the name of the disease, the mixture, age, season and place with which it is associated, as well as how to predict its future course; and he detailed various treatments, the longest being the 'general treatment'. It was translated into Latin by the Jewish translator Farağ Ibn Sālim (known as Farraguth in Latin), who was active in Sicily in the second half of the 13th century. This Latin translation was printed in Strasbourg in 1532 under the title *Tacvini Aegritvdinvm et Morborum ferme omnium Corporis humani cum curis eorundem* (The *almanac of nearly all ailments and illnesses of the human body, together with their cures*). Interestingly, John Channing (see pp48–9 above) once bought a manuscript of this text, written in *karšūnī* – that is, Arabic text in Syriac letters – and annotated it; it is now kept in the special collections of the University of Glasgow under the shelfmark MS Hunter 40 (T.1.8) (see Weston 2003).

The present text, the *Course of explanation about what man uses*, is a pharmacological handbook that discusses both simple and compound drugs. In the preface, Ibn Ǧazla provides the rationale for writing his *Course of explanation*. He wrote this work after his *Almanac* had met with approval. In it, he 'included a discussion of all drugs, drinks, and foodstuffs, and all their compounds, simples, and mixtures', yet he omitted 'simple drugs that are only known by their foreign name and whose use and shape cannot be ascertained. It is not worth mentioning them, as they are like neglected words and unused utterances'. Likewise, he omitted 'compound drugs that have no famous name'. One can therefore describe Ibn Ǧazla's approach as eminently practical. The rest of the book consists of seven chapters dealing with foodstuffs and compound drugs, and a long second part in which the simple and compound drugs that Ibn Ǧazla deemed most relevant are listed in alphabetical order.

This alphabetical arrangement can be illustrated by the beginning of the letter *fāʾ* (shown in **Fig 6.1**). It begins with *fānīd*, that is, fine white sugar; *fānīd* is originally a Persian term. Then follow *fālūḏaǧ*, from Middle Persian *pālūdag*, a kind of sweet beverage made of water, flour and honey; and *fālūḏaǧīya*. According to Ibn Ǧazla, *fālūḏaǧ* is a mixture of sugar and starch, whereas the more nourishing *fālūḏaǧīya* also contains meat. Moreover, we next see the entry for *fāšrā*, that is, white vine. The term *fāšrā* for white vine goes back to a misunderstanding: in Syriac white vine is called *ālef šārē*, but the first two letters were thought to be the Arabic article *al-*, and then separated from the word. Syriac *ālef šārē* means 'drawing a thousand (things)', and it was given to white vine because of its astringent faculty. This is also the meaning of the Persian synonym *hazār kašān*, mentioned by Ibn Ǧazla. This proliferation of synonyms and drug names in different languages illustrates both the richness of the Arabic pharmacopoeias, but also the challenges with which pharmacists were faced.

We can date the manuscript itself from the colophon. The scribe said that he finished writing it on 3 Ṣafar AH 1111, corresponding to 30 July AD 1699. It was donated to the RCP by Roy Dobbin in 1937/8.

› No 21 (MSTR1): Composite manuscript containing a short text on venesection

This manuscript is a composite one, consisting of six distinct items. It was written by a scribe in 1890, as we learn from a colophon on fol 38a. The manuscript contains 1) an epitome of *On the prevention of bodily harm in Egypt* (*Fī dafʿ maḍārr al-abdān bi-arḍ Miṣr*) by Ibn Riḍwān (d c1068); 2) a *Medical epitome known as the 'complete and perfect sword of diseases'* (*Muḫtaṣar fī l-ṭibb yuʿrafu bi-Sayf al-ʿilal ʿalā l-tamām wa-l-kamāl*) by an unknown author; 3) an *Epitome composed of the cream of what should be drawn from the art of Ṭalānūs concerning medicine* (*Muḫtaṣar muštamil ʿalā zubdat mā yağibu stiḥḍāruhū min ṣināʿat Ṭalānūs fī l-ṭibb*), again by an unknown author; 4) a short tract on phlebotomy by Ibn al-Akfānī with the title *The highest aim in the art of venesection* (*Ġāyat al-qaṣd fī sināʿat al-faṣd*); 5) two untitled medical recipes; and 6) an untitled collection of medical extracts.

Item 4 is a short tract on bloodletting by al-Akfānī. Šams al-Dīn abū ʿAbdallāh Muḥammad ibn Burhān Ibrāhīm ibn Sāʿid al-Anṣārī al-Singārī al-Miṣrī, who was known as al-Akfānī, came from the Singār, but spent most of his medical career in Cairo, where he died in 1348 of the plague. Apart from his treatise on bloodletting, he wrote on ophthalmology, home remedies, buying slaves and precious stones; moreover, he is the author of an encyclopaedia detailing 60 different branches of knowledge.

His treatise on bloodletting consists of two chapters (*bābs*). The first one deals with the definition of venesection, the conditions for its use, its benefits and its general principles. The second chapter details each of the blood vessels that can be opened, and explains how the operations are to be performed, as well as their benefits and dangers. The treatise thus concisely illustrates an important medical practice: that of venesection or phlebotomy.

We can see that Roy Dobbin, who donated this manuscript to the RCP, studied it. On the title

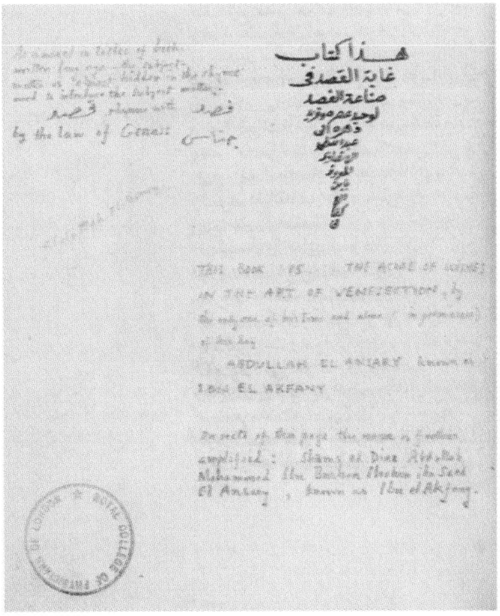

Fig 6.2, no 21 Roy Dobbin's notes on a venesection text, from composite volume, 1890.

page of this particular treatise, he jotted down two notes in pencil. The first reads:

> This book is the acme of wishes in the Art of Venesection, by the one of this time and alone (in prominence) of his day Abdullah el Ansary known as Ibn el Akfany
> On recto of this page the name is further amplified: Shâms ed Dine Abdallah Mohammed Ibn Burhan Ibrahim ibn Saed El Ansary, known as Ibn al Akfany

On the side, we find a further explanation:

> As is usual in titles of books, written long ago, the subject matter is almost hidden in the rhyme used to introduce the subject matter. *Qaṣd* ['aim'] rhymes with *faṣd* ['venesection'] by law of Genass [*ğinās*].

In other words, Dobbin translated the title, established the name of the author, and then explained the poetic quality of the title. The Arabic term *ğinās*, sometimes rendered as paronomasy, designates a linguistic feature whereby similar roots are employed for stylistic effect. In this case, as Dobbin rightly observed, '*qaṣd* rhymes with *faṣd*'.

> No 22 (Object number A643431): A cupping glass from the late 19th or early 20th century

This glass vessel has the typical shape of a cupping glass, and was probably used for this purpose. Little is known about its provenance, although it likely originated in the Islamic world. Its late date illustrates that medical practices such as cupping, described in medieval texts such as that by al-Afkānī (**no 21**), continued well into the modern period.

As described above, such cupping glasses were heated and put onto the skin of the patient in order to draw out disease matter and other waste products. The skill of the physician or practitioner who administered the procedure partly lay in his ability to identify the right spot to which to apply the cupping glass. Conversely, his inability to do so could become apparent by putting it in the wrong place. We have an interesting account of cupping performed by a charlatan in al-Ḥarīrī's *Maqāmāt* or *Assemblies* (Pormann 2005: 222–5). This collection of stories in rhymed prose and poetry depicts how the scoundrel Abū Zayd fleeces the unwitting public of their money through numerous tricks and stratagems. In episode 47, we find Abū Zayd engaged in faking to be an expert in cupping. The scene unfolds as follows: Ḥāriṯ ibn Hammām is in search of somebody who can cup him. In the market, he finds a large throng of people surrounding a cupper and a boy. The boy wants to be cupped, but has no money; the cupper refuses to carry out the procedure unless the boy pays in advance. An argument ensues and they come to blows. During the confrontation, the boy's sleeve is torn, and this leads to further confrontations. Finally, the boy begs the bystanders to give him money so that he can be cupped. He collects a significant sum. Then Ḥāriṯ asks to be cupped, but the cupper reveals that he is, in fact, Abū Zayd, the charlatan. He has no knowledge about cupping, but rather used this ruse to fleece the public of their money.

Fig 6.3, no 22 Cupping glass, late 19th or early 20th century
© Science Museum.

Although this short sketch of the episode may seem to lack sophistication, it illustrates an important point: that cupping was a current occurrence that various practitioners in the medical marketplace carried out. Moreover, the *Maqāmāt* are richly illustrated in a large number of manuscripts; in some of them, we find the scene in which cupping is performed, and it appears that Abū Zayd applies the cupping glass to the wrong part of the body. The comic effect is achieved by his incompetence. Just as he fumbles through life, so he acts as a medical practitioner: he does not know what to do. The large crowd that surrounds him highlights their gullibility: although he is plainly incompetent, they flock to Abū Zayd to have themselves cupped.

> No 23 (Object number A129015): Early-modern Persian globular bronze mortar

This is a globular bronze mortar. It is decorated in relief with men on horseback, foliage and Persian writing around rim, although the bottom is worn off. It comes from Persia and belongs to the early modern period.

There are, of course, many thousands of recipes which involve the use of a mortar to mix a drug. In most cases, the recipes do not explicitly state that one should use a mortar, but sometimes they do. The following is an example of one such case that comes from the *Medical compendium* by al-Kaskarī (fl 920s; see Pormann 2003, 2009b) and notably the section on tenesmus (*zaḥīr*), a vain effort to evacuate the bowels:

> The recipe of a medicinal powder (*safūf*) for the tenesmus (*zaḥīr*) that I took from Ḥasan; it is amazing.
>
> Take Persian marjoram, Nabatean marjoram, cumin from Kirmān, bishop's weed seed, cleansed, celery seed, galls, pomegranate peels, inner oak bark, and opium, of each one part. Crush, sieve through a hair sieve, then put it back into the mortar. Then afterwards, add the opium to it, and pound it lightly. The second dose of it is the weight of one dirham for a strong man, but the weight of four dānaq for a weak one. Do not give it to a pregnant women, and be careful with children. The food with it should be rice with oil and hump [*sanām*?]. The drink with it is quince syrup. Only take a little of it, when the time to crush it is close, as it has a somewhat strong effect.

The one active ingredient that is easily recognisable here is opium. Opium is obviously a very powerful drug, and the remarks by al-Kaskarī about dosage therefore seem quite apposite.

Selma Tibi (2006) produced a detailed study on the use of opium in ninth-century Baghdad. Opium was known as *afyūn* (from the Greek opium). Horned poppy (*māmīṯā*), for instance, was employed by physicians for ophthalmological disorders and opium for renal colics. Tibi concludes that while physicians of the earlier part of the 9th century give complicated recipes involving a great number of ingredients for a variety of disorders, medical writers in the latter part of the century have more simple recipes which are specific to one or a limited number of related diseases. This implies that over the course of the ninth century, Islamic physicians gained a greater familiarity with the use of this medicinal substance. When al-Kaskarī wrote his *Medical compendium*, it was already a tried and tested drug, the dangers of which he realised.

HERMES TRISME GISTOS ÆGYPTI
GEBER ARABS
LUMINIS GRATIÆ DEUS BONUM INFINITUM
Cherubim
Seraphim
Throni
Dominationes
Potestates
MESSIAS
SANCTA TRINITAS
Pater
Filij
S.S.
LUX IN ACCESSA
HOMO
Principatus
Virtutes
Archangeli
Angeli
Quod est Superius, est sicut id quod est inferius
In Sole et Sale Naturæ Sunt omnia.
MORIENES ROMANUS
D·O·M·A·
OSUALDI CROLLII VETERANI HASSI
BASILICA CHYMICA
CONTINENS,
Philosophicam propriâ laborum experientiâ confirmatam descriptionem et usum Remediorum Chymicorum Selectissimorum é Lumine GRATIÆ et NATURÆ DESUMPTORUM.
In fine libri additus est Autoris ejusdem Tractatus Nouus DE SIGNATURIS Rerum Internis.
ROG. BACCHON ANGLUS
Occultum fiat manifestum, et viceuersa
Per elementorum conuersionem Ternarius purificatus fiat MONAS
R. LULLIUS HISPANUS
TH. PARACELSUS GERMANUS.
LUMINIS NATURÆ BONUM FINITUM
ORA ET LABORA
REPUTANS OMNIA VANA PRÆTER AMARE DEUM ET ILLI SOLI SERVIRE.
CABALA THEOLOGICA MAGIA ASTRONOMICA HALCHYMIA MEDICA
Ignis
ANIMA
Animalia
Terra
Aqua
Aer
CORPUS
SPIRITUS
Mineralia
Vegetabilia
Cum Igne tandem Ingratiam redit Aqua.
Separate et ad maturitatem perducite.
Cum Gratia et Priuilegio S. Cæs. Maiest:

اعلم أن في داخل السماء مبدأ ما يقبل الفساد من الأشياء التي كلها واحد ترجع إليه وتنتهي إليه بعد الفساد. وهذا المبدأ هو الهيولى ومحل الكل وهو السر الأكبر ... وهذا السر الأكبر هو أصل العناصر وأمها ... ومن هذا الأصل تأتي الحياة إلى العالم وهو سر إلهي قديم مخلوق.

Know that within heaven there is a single beginning of all the things subject to corruption, to which they return in the end after being corrupted. This beginning is matter, and the place of the universe. It is the great secret ... This great secret is the basis and principle of the elements ... From this principle, life comes into the world. It is the ancient divinely created secret. (Paracelsus' explanation of the great secret in an Ottoman Arabic translation (ed Bachour 2012: 415))

7 Latin into Arabic: how Paracelsus' new chemistry filtered into the Ottoman Empire

There is a widespread idea that Islamic civilisation declined after the death of the famous philosopher and theologian al-Ġazālī in 1111. In fact, when writing his massive *History of Arabic literature* (*Geschichte der arabischen Literatur*) in the first half of the 20th century, the German orientalist Carl Brockelmann (1868–1956) characterised this post-Ġazālian period as that of the 'decline of Islamic literature' (*Niedergang der islāmischen Literatur*). There are, however, many good arguments that one can make against this notion that things went downhill after al-Ġazālī. For instance, some of the major discoveries in astronomy date from this period after al-Ġazālī's death (Saliba 2007). In medicine, Ibn al-Nafīs (d 1288) certainly proved original, as we have seen (**nos 6–7**); and one could cite the example of ʿAbd al-Laṭīf al-Baġdādī as a highly original thinker (Joosse, Pormann 2010; see also above p29). The present chapter also debunks the notion of decline and stagnation, for it shows that the exchange of new medical ideas across the Mediterranean continued into Ottoman times.

The medical theory that a balance in the four humours – black bile, yellow bile, blood and phlegm – resulted in health and an imbalance in disease remained dominant both in Europe and the Middle East throughout the Middle Ages and the Renaissance. In fact, this shared theoretical framework, nowadays called 'humoral pathology', facilitated the knowledge transfer between cultures that differed in language and religion. But humoral pathology did not remain unchallenged. In the German-speaking world, the famous physician, reformer and natural magician Philippus Aureolus Theophrastus Bombastus von Hohenheim, better known as Paracelsus (1493–1541), rejected the concepts of humoral pathology. He drew on the alchemical tradition in order to develop a new medical theory. Instead of the four humours, he developed a theory based on the interplay of the three elements mercury, salt and sulphur. These elements not only caused disease, but could also be harnessed and utilised for therapeutical purposes.

Paracelsus' new chemical medicine met with a very mixed reaction. Many regarded it as humbug and labelled Paracelsus a charlatan. But others eagerly embraced his new ideas, such as the prominent physician and educator Oswald Croll (*c*1563–1609). He composed a *Royal chemistry* (*Basilica Chymia*), in which he provides an outline of Paracelsus' ideas as he understood and accepted them. Other medical men took a more nuanced approach. Daniel Sennert (d 1637), professor of medicine at Wittenberg University, for instance, adopted some ideas of Paracelsus, notably in the area of pharmacology, but rejected others, notably the more magical and speculative aspects of his theory. Sennert wrote *Five books of medical institutions* (*Institutionum Medicinae Libri Quinque*), in which he provides an overview of the whole medical art; and he also wrote a treatise entitled *About the agreement and disagreement of the chemical authors with the Aristotelians and Galenists* (*De chymicorum cum Aristotelicis et Galenicis consensu ac dissensu*). All these works were written in Latin, the scientific *lingua franca* of early modern Europe.

Whilst these texts circulated in Europe and enjoyed a certain (though not universal) popularity, physicians at the Ottoman court also took an interest in these new works, and especially in the new medicinal substances that they contained. It has previously been thought that Ibn Sallūm (d 1669), the ḥekīmbaşi (chief physician) at the Ottoman court, translated some of these texts into Arabic, including those included in the manuscript described under **no 24** (eg Savage-Smith 1987, 2011: no 157; Shefer Mossensohn 2011). A recent and thorough study (Bachour 2012), however, found that a certain Nicolas, not Ibn Sallūm, produced these translations. As this is a new argument made in a German PhD thesis, it is useful to rehearse its main points here briefly.

In the preface to the Arabic translation of a Latin pharmacopoeia dating to September/October AD 1681 (AH 1092), the translator said the following (text ed Bachour 2012: p 73, note 203):

هذا كتاب الأقراباذين المعتبرة المستعملة في هذا الزمان في سنة اثنين وتسعين وألف في شهر رمضان المبارك. وقد شرعنا في تكميل هذا الكتاب بإلحاح بعض أفاضل الحذاق وهو رئيس الأطباء بهذه الدولة العلية أعلاه الله سردما أعني صالح أفندي بن نصر الله الحلبي قد رغبت غاية الرغبة في كتاب أطباء الأفرنجة وترجمنا أولا كتاب سنرطوس الجرماني وهو كان في معالجات الأمراض بأسرها ثم ترجمنا واختصرنا الكتاب الطب الكيمايائي ثم ترجمنا وكملنا هذا الكتاب ...

This book is the pharmacopoeia that is well regarded and widely used at this time, namely in the holy month of Ramadan, AH 1092 [September/October 1681]. We began to complete this book at the request of one of the excellent and intelligent men, namely the chief physician in this great empire – may God elevate him forever – , that is, Ṣāliḥ Afandī ibn Naṣr Allāh al-Ḥalabī [ie Ibn Sallūm; he said]: 'I have a great desire for the book by Sennert, the German.' It dealt with the treatment of all diseases. Then I translated and completed the book [entitled] *The Chemical Medicine.* Then I translated and completed this book [ie the pharmacopoeia] ...

From this preface, it would appear that the translator of the pharmacopoeia is also the translator of Sennert (eg his *Medical institutions*) and the *Chemical medicine* (that is, Croll's *Royal chemistry*). The colophon of the pharmacopoeia names the author as 'Nicolas, called the court physician' (*ṭabīb al-ḫāṣṣa*). This would imply that this Nicolas produced the Arabic translations contained in the manuscripts with the title *The new chemical medicine of Paracelsus* (*al-Ṭibb al-ğadīd al-Kīmiyāʾī taʾlīf Barākalsūs*).

Although the manuscripts of this text do not mention an author or translator, various scholars had attributed the translation to Ibn Sallūm, because it was allegedly incorporated into a larger Arabic work with the title *The utmost perfection in the treatment of the human body* (*Ġāyat al-itqān fī tadbīr badan al-insān*). Yet, Bachour (2012) argued that Ibn Sallūm did not write this Arabic version, but only the Ottoman Turkish version with the same title. The manuscripts of the *New chemical medicine* do not mention an author. Therefore, if we follow Bachour's argument, these translations were commissioned by Ibn Sallūm, who did have an avid interest in Paracelsus' ideas; however, Nicolas, not Ibn Sallūm, produced these translations from Latin into Arabic.

There is one difficulty with this argument that Bachour overlooked. The library of the Wellcome Trust in London has a manuscript of *The new chemical medicine* (WMS Arabic 24) that dates to AH 1056/7, corresponding to AD 1646/7, as we can see from the colophon:

الفراغ عن تسويد هذه الوجيزة العجيبة في
المعالجات الإنساني [!] من صناعة الطب
الكيميائي المكناة بإساغريا للحكيم براكلسوس
الجرماني في السنة السابعة من الجلوس السلطاني
نهار العشرين من المحرم بعد نصف المائة الأولى
من الألف الثاني بيد ...

> The drafting of this wonderful abridgment about human treatments through the chemical medical art, called 'spagiria' by Paracelsus, the German physician, was completed in the seventh year of the accession to the sultanate on 20 Muḥarram 1050 (ie 12 May AD 1640) by ...

This means that this copy must have been written some time between March 1646 and February 1647, some 35 years before 'Nicolas, the court physician' penned his translation of the pharmacopoeia. Moreover, one of the sources for the pharmacopoeia is the so-called *Antidotarium Nicolai*, or *Nicolas' pharmacopoeia*; could there therefore be some confusion here?

Be that as it may, the fact remains that at the Ottoman court, prominent physicians such as Ibn Sallūm followed the new medical developments in Europe with interest. And new medical knowledge found its way from Latin into Arabic, just as new philosophical ideas expressed in Greek during the Renaissance were translated into Arabic. It is important, however, to understand the scope of this Latin-Arabic translation movement, and its impact on medical theory. Emilie Savage-Smith had already seen that the *New chemical medicine* represented a mixture of the old and the new: certain new diseases are described here for the first time in Arabic, including scurvy and chlorosis. Moreover, many new 'chemical' remedies become available in Arabic for the first time. Distillation, for instance, features prominently here. On the other hand, we find the theoretical framework of humoral pathology, inherited from the earlier tradition, intact. For example, Dāwūd al-Anṭākī (d 1599), who had written a medical compendium called *Dāwūd's handbook* (*Taḏkirat Dāwūd*), remains an important source. Therefore, whereas Paracelsus deliberately attacked the medical establishment and its Galenic ideas, the physicians at the Ottoman court remained much more conciliatory: they did not endeavour to do away with Galenic medicine, but rather tried to incorporate new insights about diseases and their cures into the framework of humoral pathology.

Here, the chapter on melancholy from the *Utmost perfection* can serve as an example (Bachour 2012: 70–71). Melancholy is a disease caused by an excess of black bile (*mélaina cholḗ*), as its name already suggests. As such, it is an ailment that exemplifies particularly well the system of humoral pathology, in which black bile is one of the four humours. In the Turkish version of the *Utmost perfection*, authored by Ibn Sallūm, we find the familiar division of melancholy into three types – general, hypochandriac and encephalic – that goes back to Galen's treatise *On the affected parts*, who probably adopted it from Rufus of Ephesus (Pormann 2008: 257–78; 2014). In the Arabic version, the author follows a more simplified model. The important point, however, is that in neither version does the author challenge the humoral underpinnings of this disease.

Ibn Sallūm's patronage extended beyond the works of Croll and Sennert, and also included other texts popular in early modern Europe. They include, for instance, the *Special* and *General pharmacopoeia* (*Antidotarium speciale*; *Antidotarium generale*) by the Swiss doctor Johann Jacob Wecker (1528–86) and works on fever by the Spanish physician Luis de Mercado (Ludouicus Mercatus, 1513–99). Moreover, many of these texts were translated into Ottoman Turkish, often via Arabic, so that the new medical ideas reached new audiences. Therefore, although the fundamental tenets of humoral pathology remained largely unchallenged at the Ottoman court, the physicians there certainly were *au fait* with what happened in the Latin-speaking world. A motor for this exchange of ideas was, again, translation. Even if Ibn Sallūm did not translate from Latin into Arabic directly himself, it does not detract from the fact that his interest in European medicine played a crucial part in the transmission of medical knowledge.

Further reading

The fundamental study on Paracelsus at the Ottoman court is now Bachour (2012), who offers many fresh insights, but unfortunately writes in German. The pioneering work by Emilie Savage-Smith (1987) remains the best available scholarship in English; see also Shefer Mossensohn (2011). On Paracelsus himself, see the highly readable Webster (2008).

Exhibition items

> **No 24** (MSTR33): An early modern manuscript containing *The new chemical medicine of Paracelsus*

Al-Ṭibb al-ǧadīd al-Kīmiyāʾī taʾlīf Barākalsūs is an Arabic abridged translation of two works by German physicians, Daniel Sennert (d 1637) and Oswald Croll (*c*1563–1609).

The first part (pp1–122) contains the abridged translation of Sennert's *About the agreement and disagreement of the chemical authors with the Aristotelians and Galenists* and his *Medical institutions*. Yet the translator selected those chapters that dealt with the more theoretical and practical aspects of chemistry and spagyric, whilst omitting the more magical aspects or those having specifically Christian references (Bachour 2012: 107–34).

The first part is divided into a short introduction (*muqaddima*) by the translator and four books (*maqālas*): the first deals with 'theoretical medicine' (*al-ṭibb al-naẓarī*); the second with 'the foundations of chemical medicine' (*asās al-ṭibb al-kīmāʾī*); the third with 'how to prepare, dissolve, and crush drugs according to their method' (that of the Paracelsians) (*kayfīyat tadbīri l-adwiyati wa-taḥlīlihā wa-taftītihā ʿalā ṭarīqatihim*); and the fourth with 'particular procedures' (*al-ʿamalīyāt bi-qawlin ǧuzʾīyin*). The introduction and the first three books are mainly taken from Sennert's *About the agreement and disagreement*. The fourth book contains many recipes and practical preparations; they come for the most part from Sennert's *Medical institutions*, notably part three ('On the composition of drugs' [*De compositione medicamentorum*]), section three '*On the types of drugs*' [*De formis medicamentorum*]).

In the introduction (opposite page (fol 21a–b)), Ibn Sallūm says the following about his topic (tr Mingana modified):

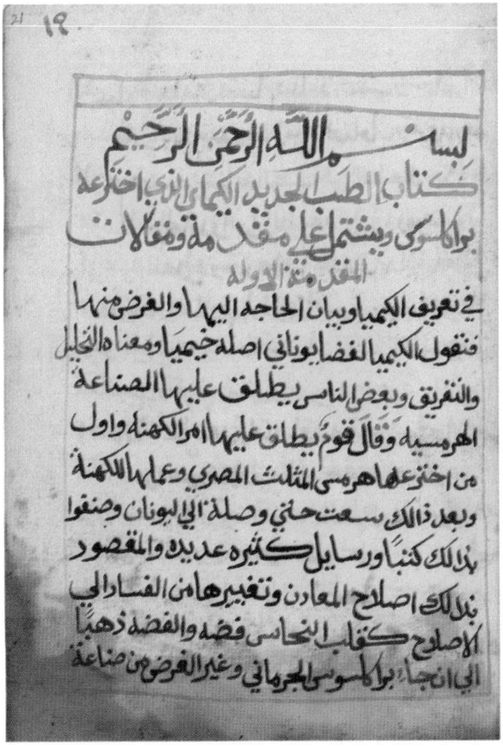
21 ١٢

بسم الله الرحمن الرحيم
كتاب الطب الجديد الكيماوي الذي اخترعه
براكلسوس ويشتمل على مقدمة ومقالات
المقدمة الاولى
في تعريف الكيميا وبيان الحاجة اليها والغرض منها
فنقول الكيميا لفظ يوناني اصله خيميا ومعناه التحليل
والتفريق وبعض الناس يطلق عليها الصناعة
الهرمسية وقال قوم يطلق عليها امر الكهنة واول
من اخترعها هرمس المثلث المصري وعلمها الكهنة
وبعد ذلك شاعت حتى وصلت الى اليونان وصنفوا
بذلك كتبا ورسايل كثيرة عديدة والمقصود
بذلك اصلاح المعادن وتغييرها من الفساد الى
الاصلاح كقلب النحاس فضة والفضة ذهبا
الى ان جا براكلسوس الجرماني وغير الغرض من صناعة

Fig 7.2, no 24 ***The new chemical medicine of Paracelsus*****, 17th century.**

> The word al-Kīmiyā is Greek, and its root is Ḫīmīyā, meaning analysis and separation. Some men term it the Hermetic art, and people call it the secret of the Priests. Later, it was divulged and came to the Greeks. They composed many books and treatises about it. Then it was transferred to the Muslims, and they wrote many books about it, with the aim to purify metals and change them from adulteration to purity; examples include changing copper into silver, or silver into gold. Then Paracelsus, the German, came and altered the purpose of the art of Kīmiyā. He produced from its elements the art of medicine which he named *Spagiria* in Latin, the meaning being a combination and separation of unlike things.

The translator is, of course, right in saying that al-*kīmiyā* is ultimately a Greek word; it comes from *chēmeia* or *chymeia* in the sense of 'smelting'. Likewise, he correctly explains the term 'spagiria', originally coined by Paracelsus: like so many modern terms in medicine, it is modelled on Greek words, but never existed as such in Classical Greek. The two elements of the word 'spagiria' are *spáō* ('to draw') and *ageírō* ('to collect') in the sense of separating and composing, respectively. Interestingly, this passage is missing from the version edited by Šihāda (1997). This suggests that the textual tradition is richer than previously thought, as Bachour also confirms (2012: 108–9).

The second part of this *New chemical medicine* is again an abridged translation, this time of Croll's *Royal chemistry*. At the beginning, the translator explains concisely what this treatise is (fol 74a, corresponding to ed Šihāda 1997: 203):

وقد ألف في صناعة الطب الكيمائي قروليوس
كتابا مختصرا مفيدا لملك زمانه مشتملا على
مقالتين فأردنا أن ننقله من اللاطينية إلى العربي
ليكون به تمام النفع وسمى هذا المختصر كيميا
باسيليقا يعني الكيمياء الملكية

> Crollius wrote an abridged book dedicated to the king of his time about the art of chemical medicine. It consists of two books (*maqālas*). We wanted to translate it from Latin into Arabic, so that it would be useful [to Arabic speakers]. He called this abridgment *Chymia Basilica*, meaning 'Royal chemistry'.

The two books that the translator mentions deal with general principles and particular remedies respectively.

> No 25 (copy no 13655, D2/61-f-10(1)): ***Royal chemistry*** **by German Paracelsian Oswald Croll, published in Frankfurt am Main in 1611**

Oswald Croll was a German physician (1560–1609) who studied in Marburg, where he took his MD, but also at other universities, including Heidelberg, Strasbourg and Geneva. During his career, he enjoyed the patronage of various aristocratic households, and he spent the last decade and a half of his life in Prague, where he sometimes ministered to Rudolf II, the Holy Roman Emperor, who was interested in the occult arts. Croll himself developed a strong attachment to the doctrine of Paracelsus, and he wrote the very influential *Royal chemistry*, first published in Frankfurt am Main in 1609.

The frontispiece of the second 1611 edition (see **Fig 7.1**) illustrates the world of ideas that many Paracelsians inhabited. The long title runs as follows *The royal chemistry by Oswald Croll, the old man from Hesse; it contains a philosophical description, confirmed by his own experience and experimentations, and application of selected chemical drugs, taken from the light of grace and nature* (*Osualdi Crollii Veterani Hassi Basilica Chymica continens philosophicam propriâ laborum experimentiâ confirmatam descriptionem et usum remediorum chymicorum selectissimorum a lumine Gratiae et Naturae*). Above the title in the centre, we see a representation of the Holy Trinity as a triangle, in the middle of which is written the tetragrammaton (יהוה), God's name in Hebrew. On the outside of the circle, we read the adage: 'The good of the Light of Grace is infinite' (*Luminis Gratiae bonum infinitum*). This corresponds to the adage around the circle below the title, which reads: 'The good of the Light of Nature is infinite' (*Luminis Naturae bonum infinitum*). Inside this outer circle, we find the pious admonition: 'Pray and work, reflecting on the fact that all things are vain, except to love God and to serve Him alone' (*Ora et labora reputans omnia vana praeter amare deum et illi soli servire*). On the left and the right sides, we find six figures who represent the most important influences for

Fig 7.3 Engraving of a portrait of Paracelsus.

Croll's chemical medicine. They are the Egyptian Hermes Trismegistus ('thrice great'), the mystical father of alchemy, here wearing a turban; the Arab Ğābir ibn Ḥayyān, an alchemical author of the 8th century, whose life is shrouded in mystery; the Roman Morienus, an apocryphal author of the *Book on the composition of alchemy* (*Liber de compositione alchemiae*), translated in 1144 by Robert of Chester; the Englishman Roger Bacon (*c*1214–92), who had a strong interest in astrology; the Spaniard Raymond Lull (1232–1315), alleged author of a corpus of alchemical works; and finally Paracelsus himself.

We can therefore see the various influences that come together in the chemical medicine as developed by Paracelsus and Croll. Protestant religion plays a prominent role, as does the mysticism of the Christian Cabbala. But the so-called occult sciences – alchemy, astrology, magic – also play a major role. Interestingly, when Croll's work is translated into Arabic (and thence into Ottoman Turkish), these occult and religious aspects occupy a much more restricted place; the physicians at the Ottoman court were more interested in the new medical preparations.

> **No 26** (no 1977-293): Early 20th-century alembic and cucurbit in blue glass, from Isfahan, Iran

> **No 27** (object number A72847): A medieval glass beaker, possibly used as an alembic

In the medieval world, distillation was generally carried out with the help of a cucurbit, an alembic and a receiving flask (Maddison, Savage-Smith 1997: i 48–57). The cucurbit (Arabic *qarʿ*, lit 'gourd') is, as its name suggests, a gourd-shaped glass vessel, often with a rounded bottom, that narrows a little towards the top and is open there. Onto the open top one places the alembic. The English word alembic is a borrowing from the Arabic *al-anbīq*, which itself consists of the Arabic article '*al-*' and a loan word derived from Greek *ámbix*, also meaning 'alembic'. The alembic consists of two main elements: a round top with a longish opening at the bottom that fits the cucurbit; and a tube that delivers the condensate accumulating at the top. This tube is then put into a receiving flask.

Normally, the cucurbit is filled with the liquid that is to be distilled, and then put onto a heat source such as a furnace filled with sand. The alembic is placed on top of it, and both cucurbit and alembic are tilted a little bit to the side of the tube. The tube is put into the receiving flask. As the liquid in the alembic is heated, it evaporates. Because the top of the alembic is cooler than the bottom of the cucurbit, a condensate forms there, and the drops accumulate gradually and run into the tube, and thence into the receiving flask.

The set of matching alembic and cucurbit displayed in **no 26** is made of blue glass. The alembic measures 44 cm in length, 14 cm in height and 11 cm in width, whereas the cucurbit is 26 cm long and has a diameter of 10 cm. This set comes from Isfahan, in modern-day Iran, and dates back to the early 20th century. It was acquired in Isfahan in the summer of 1975 from an alchemist and physician who was still practising in the traditional way; he was called Azad Manesh. The set is remarkable in that its exact provenance is known; most objects of this kind were acquired in a way that does not allow their origin to be traced. The cucurbit was wrapped in clay whilst in use, but this clay has crumbled away.

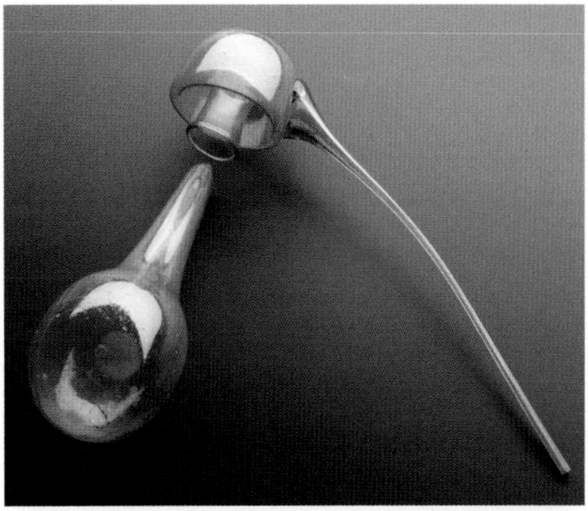

Fig 7.4 (top) Alembic and cucurbit in blue glass, Iran, early 20th century © Science Museum.

Fig 7.5 (bottom) Glass beaker, possibly used as an alembic, Islamic, 12–13th century © Science Museum.

Whereas the set displayed in **no 26** is of a fairly recent date, the glass beaker shown as **no 27** probably dates to the 12th or 13th centuries. It rises to a height of 5.5 cm and possesses a width of 10.2 cm. One should note the spot projecting from below the rim. It could have been used as an alembic.

Fig 8.1 Egypt, the Red Sea and Arabia, *Cosmographie universelle*, Thevet, 1575.

Nam & Scientiae Liberales ritèque institutae, diù ante vocari solebant a Nostris Studia Arabum & Arabica Studia, veluti denominata à gente ac locis ubi tunc solùm seriò colebantur.

Previously, the liberal and correctly taught sciences were for a long time called by us [English] *'the studies of the Arabs' or 'Arabic studies', as if they took their name from the only people and places where they were then cultivated in a serious way.* (John Selden (1642: 156; tr with modifications Burnett 2009))

8 Collectors and cataloguers during the Renaissance and the Enlightenment

This opening quotation by a prominent 17th-century scholar shows that intellectuals were well aware of the debt that they owed to the Arabic scientific tradition. Renaissance medicine was no exception here: Arabic works in Latin translation were still part of medicine, being taught in the universities and practised by physicians all over Europe. England was no exception here. Many of the leading doctors such as Thomas Linacre (1460–1524) and John Caius (1510–73) studied on the continent, where Avicenna (Ibn Sīnā) and Ioannitius (Ḥunayn ibn Isḥāq) were standard textbooks. Arabic works in Latin translation were used less and less over the course of the 17th and 18th centuries, as new ideas replaced old ones and the framework of humoral pathology began to unravel. This said, the interest in Arabic learning continued, and even increased in the 17th and 18th centuries, as the example of the apothecary turned orientalist John Channing illustrates (see **no 16**).

Two figures with a strong interest in all things Arabic are particularly closely connected to the RCP. First, there is John Selden (1584–1654), a prominent lawyer, historian and linguistic scholar, whose quotation about the sciences being simply called 'sciences of the Arabs' opened this chapter. The second figure is Henry Wild (1684–1734), the 'Arabian tailor' whom we have already encountered above (p49). Selden bequeathed 11 oriental medical manuscripts to the RCP on 9 April 1655 and 1 Feb 1655 or 1656; moreover, a fellow of the college by the name of Dr William Rant (1604–53) donated six Arabic books. Selden was also responsible for the acquisition of books from the collection of Isaac Faragi in 1648, which comprised both Hebrew and Persian manuscripts and many books. Later, Wild catalogued the Arabic manuscripts in the RCP's collections, thus providing a first description of the material.

But who were John Selden and Henry Wild, both so intimately linked to the history of the collection? John Selden (1584–1654; see Christianson 2008) was born in Sussex and studied at Oxford, before taking up the law: he first joined Clifford's Inn and then the Inner Temple in his late teens. In London, Selden did not only practise law, but also became an impressive linguist, mastering not only modern languages such as French, German, Spanish and Italian, and the classical ones (Latin, Greek), but also a number of semitic and oriental tongues, including Hebrew, Aramaic, Ethiopic, Arabic and Persian. He took a great interest in legal history, first working on Roman, Canon and old Anglo-Saxon law, but soon branching out into Jewish law and Jewish history more generally. His *On the Syrian gods* (*De Dis Syris*), first published in London in 1617 and repeatedly reprinted, discussed, for instance, ideas about gods in the ancient Levant, drawing on a large variety of oriental sources. He also collected a substantial number of manuscripts over the course of his life. Apart from the 11 manuscripts on medical matters that he donated to the RCP, he bequeathed his other, non-medical oriental manuscripts to the Bodleian Library in Oxford.

The 11 manuscripts that Selden donated are MSS Tritton 2 (**no 28**), 4 (an abridgment of a medical handbook), 12 (**no 5**), 14 (a Persian compendium on medicine based on Avicenna's *Canon*, entitled *Qānūnǧā fī l-ṭibb*), 22 (**no 1**), 23 (**no 29**), 24 (The *Almanac of health* [*Taqwīm al-ṣiḥḥa*] by Ibn Buṭlān [d after 1063]), 26 (a second copy of Ibn Ǧazla's *Course of explanation about what man uses*; cf **no 20**), 28 (a book on simple drugs by al-Kutubī, written in 1311), 50 (a Persian medical encyclopaedia, entitled *Treasure of King Ḫʷarizm* (*Ḏaḫīra-yi Ḫʷarizmšāhī*) and 63 (a medical treatise in verse, called *Consolation of spirits* [*Tarwīḥ al-arwāḥ*]).

Henry Wild (1684–1734) grew up in Norwich, where he attended a local grammar school. Unable to afford the expense of going to university, he was apprenticed to a tailor for seven years and worked another seven as a journeyman. This economic hardship did not prevent him from studying in his spare time: he took a notable interest in the 'oriental' languages, among them Hebrew, Arabic and Persian; and he continued to make progress in Greek. Through a quirk of fate, he attracted the attention of Humphrey Prideaux (1648–1724), the dean of Norwich and author of a *Life of Mahomet* (1697). Dr Prideaux then sponsored him to go up to Oxford and, although not a formal member of the University, he was admitted to the Bodleian Library. He sustained himself by translating and instructing students in oriental languages. Around 1720, he moved to London under the patronage of Dr Richard Mead (1673–1754), an influential RCP fellow, as well as an accomplished scholar and collector. During his first year in London, he catalogued 10 out of the 11 manuscripts donated by Selden, presumably at the request of his new patron. MS Tritton 12 (**no 5**), now the oldest manuscript in the collection, was omitted for unknown reasons. We have a personal account of one of his student (recorded in Munday 1809: iii 266–9), who reports that Wild was known as the 'Arabian tailor' at Oxford. Although his learning was profound, he never published anything in his lifetime, and only his translation of 'Mahomet's journey to heaven' appeared posthumously.

The Arabic collections also attracted the interest of the orientalist and lexicographer Edmund Castell (1606–85; see Toomer 2008). He spent a large fortune on printing a heptaglot Bible (a bible in which the text is arranged in seven parallel columns) and a heptaglot lexicon, the seven languages being Hebrew, Samaritan, Chaldee (ie Aramaic), Syriac, Arabic, Ethiopian and Persian. He drew on the oriental collections of the RCP while researching his *Lexicon*, which was eventually finished in 1669. His polyglot publishing efforts nearly bankrupted him; and when the *Lexicon* finally appeared, it attracted relatively little interest. (See RCP, MS4145 Comitia vol iv, 28 Mar 1659, 5 Feb 1659/60; 16 Apr and 25 Jun 1660.)

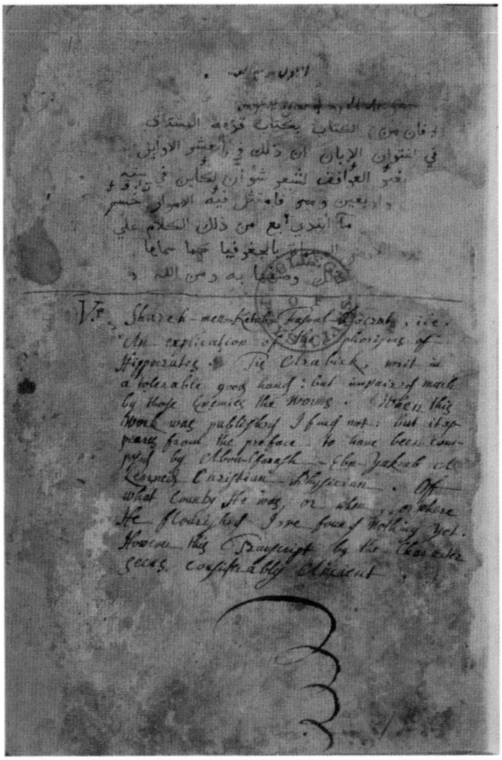

Fig 8.2, no 28 Notes by Henry Wild on the *Commentary on the aphorisms of Hippocrates*, 18th century.

Further reading

Nancy Siraisi (1987) produced a seminal work on the role of Avicenna during the Renaissance, and has continued to publish influential works on the period (eg 2001, 2007). Alistair Hamilton (2011) produced a particularly attractive book – both visually and intellectually – about the European interest in Arabic studies (with further references). And Pormann (2011c) argued that the Renaissance amnesia regarding the Arabo-Islamic legacy in the West was neither innocent nor value-free, but has to be seen in the context of an ideology that aspired to religious, linguistic and ethnic purity.

Exhibition items

> **No 28** (MSTR2): *Commentary on the aphorisms* **by the Christian physician Ibn al-Quff, donated by John Selden, with notes by Henry Wild**

Henry Wild catalogued this manuscript (shown left) in the following terms (fol 1a):

> V. Shareh-men-ketab-Fasoul-Bocrat, ie An explication of the Aphorisms of Hippocrates. Tis Arabick writ in a tolerable good hand: but impaired much by those Enemies, the worms. When this work was published I find not: but it appeares from the preface to have been composed by Abou-lfaragh-Ebn-Yakoub A learned Christian Physician. Of what country He was, or when or where He flourished I've found nothing yet. However this Transcript by the Character seems considerably Ancient.

Therefore, Wild first provides the Arabic title of the book in transliteration (*Šarḥ min kitāb Fuṣūl Buqrāṭ*) according to his own conventions. Then he translates it, comments on the state of the manuscript, and tries to ascertain who the author was. He takes his name from the beginning of the text where it appears (Abū l-Farağ ibn Yaʿqūb, known as Ibn al-Quff).

In fact, this manuscript contains one of the many commentaries on the Hippocratic *Aphorisms* (Joosse, Pormann 2012). The *Aphorisms* proved extremely popular already in antiquity; the first aphorism (see Introduction, p5) is still well known today, and not only among doctors. Some seem quite reasonable, such as *Aphorism* v 34 'If a pregnant woman suffers from a lot of diarrhoea, then there is the danger that she will miscarry' (Γυναικὶ ἐν γαστρὶ ἐχούσῃ, ἣν ἡ κοιλίη πουλλὰ ῥυῇ, κίνδυνος ἐκτρῶσαι.); others appear more outlandish, such as 'Eunuchs do not suffer from gout, nor do they become bald' (Εὐνοῦχοι οὐ ποδαγριῶσιν, οὐδὲ φαλακροὶ γίνονται). Whatever we may nowadays think about these aphorisms, their popularity certainly extended to the Arab world, for between the 9th and the 16th century, more than 20 commentaries on the *Aphorisms* were written in Arabic by authors belonging to different religions and countries. They based their own commentaries on that written by Galen and translated into Arabic in Ḥunayn ibn Isḥāq's workshop.

The present commentary is by far the largest and longest of them all. As we have already seen, it was written by Ibn al-Quff, a Christian physician from Syria who died in 1286. Ibn al-Quff approaches his task of commenting by dividing it into topics of discussion (*mabāḥiṯ*). Normally, he first investigates how the aphorism in question is connected to the previous and the following ones (what he calls the 'connection' (*ṣila*)). Then he turns to the other topics that seem interesting to him. Some of these questions look somewhat scholastic to the modern reader: al-Quff does not shy from splitting hairs.

The present manuscript does not contain the whole (and very long) commentary, but only the first one and a half (out of seven) books. In fact, it breaks off towards the end of the commentary on aphorism ii 24, dealing with critical days, that is, days on which the crisis of a disease supervenes.

Fig 8.3 Portrait of John Selden (1584–1654), Robert White after unknown artist, 1683.

> No 29 (MSTR23): Arabic manuscript of the *Hippocratic treatments*, donated by John Selden, with notes by Henry Wild

This is another manuscript for which we have Wild's catalogue entry; it reads:

> Ketâb belmoäleját-fi-elâl-Ain, ie, Hippocrates on the several diseases of the Eyes, with their Cures. Tis Arabick writ in a tolerable good hand; & is divided into fifty four chapters. This Version (or perhaps this present copy) was published Anno Hejhra 761; Anno Christi 1359. Where I find the date the paper is so impaired, that I can only gess that the Translators name was sheik Mohammed-Ebn-Gâg.

As in the previous item (**no 28**), Wild first transliterates the title, then translates it and makes some general remarks about the manuscript and its content. In this case, however, we also have notes by Arthur Stanley Tritton (1881–1973), the professor of Arabic at the School of Oriental and African Studies. Tritton (1951) catalogued the manuscripts at the RCP, and in the case of this manuscript, he took copious notes that are now bound with it. In the first and longest note, he took Wild to task for thinking that this manuscript was an Arabic translation of a Hippocratic text, saying:

> Mr Wild is greatly mistaken in ascribing this piece to Hippocrates; as will appear by the following list of medicines I find in it; not known in the time of Hippocrates:

There follows a list of simple drugs such as camphor, tamarind, ginger etc, after which Tritton continues:

> And if this is not sufficient; the following list of Authors quoted in it will amount to an absolute proof of Mr W[il]d.'s mistake.

He then goes on to list both Greek and Arabic authorities, quoted here, and continues:

> So that it is out of doubt, this book was written by some Arabian or Jew, as late as the 13. century. Which makes one surprized at Mr Wild's giving such an account as we find entred by him in this book.
>
> But to compleat his tale, he has furnished us with the name of the person who translated it from the original Greek into Arabic, which is no other than the name of the owner of the book writt' in the blank leaf at the beginning under the title page in the usual manner. The writing imports that this book was transferred into the possession (ie became the property) of Ebn Mostafi Ben Abdalla Ben Alyas Scheich Mohammed in the year 761, ie AD 1360. This is the name of Mr Wild's translator. But the book being most apparently written in Arabic wanted no translation.

In other words, not only does Tritton establish that this work was not by Hippocrates, but also that Wild's assumption about the translator was wrong; Wild confused the owner of the manuscript with the translator.

Since Tritton's work, a good deal of progress has been made. We now know that the *Hippocratic treatments* (*al-Muʿālağāt al-Buqrāṭīya*) is a medical handbook (*kunnāš*) by Abū l-Ḥasan al-Ṭabarī, a physician active in the second half of the 10th century. This handbook consists of 10 treatises (*maqālas*), each further subdivided into chapters (*faṣls*). After the first treatise on general principles, the author arranges his material roughly from tip to toe, beginning with trichological disorders and ending with intestinal conditions (Ambjörn 2011 with further references). The present manuscript only contains the fourth treatise on ophthalmological disorders. There are a number of other manuscripts that only preserve this fourth treatise, and this suggests that it was appreciated as a useful handbook on ophthalmology in its own right (for other copies, see eg, Savage-Smith 2011, no 48A, 48C).

Fig 9.1 Modern Cairo © iStockphoto.com

It is the fate of most to be entirely forgotten within a few years after death, and this is particularly true of those spending most of their professional lives abroad.

JL Thornton and PC Want (1974: 1087) about Roy Dobbin (1873–1939)

9 Modern collectors

The last manuscripts came into the collection of the RCP in the first half of the 20th century, and notably during the period between the two world wars. The most significant donor was Roy Dobbin, who spent a large part of his career in Cairo, Egypt. He remains largely forgotten, as this opening quotation illustrates, although he gave 31 manuscripts to the RCP, that is half its present collection. Cyril Elgood (1892–1970), who lived in Persia from 1925 to 1931, is the second most important donor in modern times, having given 10 oriental manuscripts to the RCP, as well as one manuscript containing his English translation of a Persian medical manual entitled *The mirror of health* (*Mirʾāt al-ṣiḥḥa*). The two donors, both RCP fellows, represent well the two important poles of the Islamic world at that time. Egypt was the cultural and intellectual centre to which most Arabs looked for inspiration and entertainment, and Persia – which the Shah, 'enamoured by the racial theories popularised by Adolf Hitler' (Gelvin 2008: 15), renamed Iran in 1934 – remained the focal point of the Persian-speaking world. Both Dobbin and Elgood also lived at 'empire's end', when different colonial powers vied for cultural influence (Dueck 2010).

Roy Dobbin studied medicine at Trinity College Dublin (Thornton, Want 1974). Whilst in Dublin, he still mainly busied himself with pathology, but he also took an interest in gynaecology and obstetrics. In 1906, he arrived in Cairo, where he occupied the position of professor of obstetrics and gynaecology at Cairo University, and senior obstetric surgeon and gynaecologist at the famous Qaṣr al-ʿAynī Hospital. During the First World War, he served in the Royal Army Medical Corps, but returned afterwards to Cairo. It was there that he remained for the rest of his life, and there that he also built up an important private library: he avidly collected books and manuscripts, and developed a particular interest in the history of gynaecology and obstetrics among the Arabs. In this way, Dobbin combined not only clinical practice with medical teaching, but also pursued his interests in the history of medicine. After his death in 1939, Cairo University founded a medal in his name and named a gynaecological ward in the hospital after him.

Like Dobbin, Max Meyerhof (1874–1945) was a practising physician and medical historian. Meyerhof came from Hildesheim in Germany, but went to Egypt in 1903, where he headed the Khedivial Ophthalmological Clinic. Again like Dobbin, he returned to his homeland during the First World War and joined the medical corps. After the war, he stayed another five years in Germany, working as an ophthalmologist, but then went back to Cairo to spend the rest of his life there. Meyerhof concerned himself in particular with the care for Egypt's poor, but was also active in both the German and the Jewish communities. Meyerhof also emerged as the leading authority in the area of the history of medicine in the medieval Islamic world, editing numerous ophthalmological texts for the first time and publishing widely on the topic in four languages, namely German, French, English and Arabic.

In Cairo, Roy Dobbin became acquainted with Meyerhof. They shared an interest in both medicine and medical history, and both had modern copies of medieval manuscripts made, such as the one containing al-Baladī's *Book on pregnant women, and children* (**no 33**). A letter in another manuscript (**no 31**) on pharmacology testifies to the fact that Meyerhof shared his discoveries generously with his colleagues: he sent the precious manuscript to Dobbin, who studied it further. Dobbin and Meyerhof must have known each other before the First World War, given their profession and interest. We might wonder how they felt about having served opposing armies when they found each other again after the Great War.

Whereas Dobbin and Meyerhof mainly worked on Arabic material, Cyril Elgood (1892–1970) took a special interest in Persian works. After attending Oxford, he moved to India in 1914 to serve in the British Army, but, owing to ill health, he went back to London to study medicine at St Bartholomew's Hospital. He travelled to Persia in 1925, where he looked after the medical needs of the British legation, and eventually even became honorary physician to the Shah. After his return from Persia, he published a number of books on medical history in Persia, the most substantial being his *A medical history of Persia and the eastern caliphate* (Cambridge, 1951) and his *Safavid medical practice* (London, 1970).

Dobbin donated 22 Arabic (Tritton 1, 5, 7, 8, 11, 15, 16–18, 20–21, 25, 27, 29, 31–2, 34–5, 37–40) and nine Persian (Tritton 43–4, 46, 49, 51–2, 59–61) manuscripts to the RCP, whereas Elgood gave it one Arabic (Tritton 19) and nine Persian (Tritton 42, 45, 47, 53–58) manuscripts. Dobbin's and Elgood's contribution to the collections of the RCP was therefore immense, and it is hoped that their names will not be forgotten.

In 1950, the RCP decided to catalogue its oriental manuscripts; this wish arose in the context of refurbishing the library and taking stock of its holdings in the post-war period. Elgood was first approached to undertake this task, but in January 1951, the RCP decided to entrust it to Tritton, whose summary catalogue appeared in the same year in the *Journal of the Royal Asiatic Society*. All Arabic, Persian and Turkish manuscripts still bear the shelfmark that Tritton assigned to them (and that are used throughout this catalogue).

Further reading

For a general history of the RCP, see Clark *et al* (1964–2005). The catalogue by Tritton (1951) is rather terse, and says little about the collection as such. Thornton and Want (1974) reconstruct Dobbin's life through the use of archival material and oral accounts.

Exhibition items

> No 30 (MSTR35): A hitherto unidentified medieval pharmacological manuscript, donated by Dobbin

This manuscript contains a treatise on pharmacology, but unfortunately the leaves have been bound erroneously. The following topics are discussed in the manuscript (in each case, I provide the number of the chapter (*maqāla*) and the title): chapter eight on alopecia (fol 1a); chapter one on states of the head (fol 5b); chapter two on the eye (fol 7a); chapter three on the ear (fol 15a); chapter five on the mouth and throat (fol 22a); chapter six on stomach weakness (fol 23b); chapter four on toothache (fol 31a); chapter seven on preserves (*murabbayāt*) (fol 33b); chapter eight on tablets (*aqrāṣ*) (fol 37a); chapter nine on young wine (*sulāfāt*) and berries (*ḥubūb*) (fol 42b), chapter two on 'holy remedies' (*iyārāǧāt*, a type of purgative) (fol 62b); purging electuaries (*ǧawārišnāt*) (fol 69a); chapter five on electuaries (*laᶜūqāt*) (fol 77a); chapter six on juices (*ašriba*) and concentrated juices (*rubūb*) (fol 80a); chapter eleven on ointments (*marāhim*) (fol 89a); chapter seven on joint pain, gout and sciatica (fol 99b).

The chapters appear to belong to two different parts of the same work, or perhaps to two different works. This is apparent for two reasons. First, the same chapter number appears twice in this manuscript; for instance there is a 'chapter two on the eye' (*al-maqāla al-ṯāniya fī l-ᶜayn*) and a 'chapter two on holy remedies' (*al-maqāla al-ṯāniya fī l-iyārāǧāt*). Second, the earlier chapters appear to be arranged from tip to toe, beginning with the head, eye, ear and so on, whereas the later chapters deal with types of compound drugs, such as purging remedies and electuaries.

The paper and writing of the manuscript appear to suggest a relatively early date, possibly dating back to the 13th century. Roy Dobbin donated this manuscript to the College. He provided the following title and short description in pencil on the first leaf:

> PHARMACOPOEIA
>
> beginning & end missing. Must be very old, as only Greek & early Arabic Authors are quoted. (IXth cent Baghdad).

Future studies will have to determine what text exactly this manuscript contains.

> No 31 (MSTR7): A pharmacological manuscript from the mid-17th century, donated by Dobbin, with a letter from Max Meyerhof

This manuscript contains a pharmacological treatise by Abū Saᶜīd Ibrāhīm ibn Muḥammad al-Maġribī (fl c1650) with the title *Victory in the treatment of different types of diseases and complaints* (*Kitāb al-Fatḥ fī l-tadāwī li-ṣunūf al-amrāḍ wa-l-šakāwī*). It lists 550 medical substances in alphabetical order with descriptions, dosages and effects arranged in tables. We learn from the colophon that this particular manuscript was copied in Rabīᶜ II AH 1058 (corresponding to May AH 1648) by Aḥmad al-Azharī, presumably an Egyptian with connections to the al-Azhar Mosque in Cairo. It is therefore a copy that is contemporaneous with the lifetime of its author, and as such of particular value, especially since it appears to be complete.

The fact that Roy Dobbin donated the manuscript

Fig 9.2, no 31 Max Meyerhof's notes on *Victory in the treatment of different types of diseases and complaints*, 20th century.

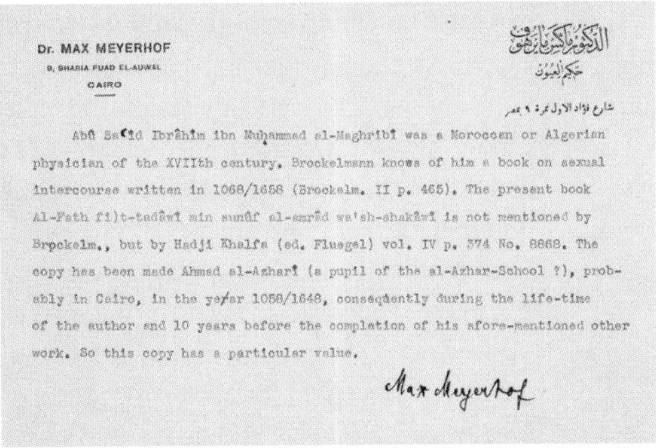
Dr. MAX MEYERHOF
9, SHARIA FUAD EL-AUWAL
CAIRO

الدكتور ماكس مايرهوف
حكيم العيون
شارع فؤاد الاول نمرة ٩ بمصر

Abû Saᶜîd Ibrâhîm ibn Muḥammad el-Maghribî was a Moroccan or Algerian physician of the XVIIth century. Brockelmann knows of him a book on sexual intercourse written in 1068/1658 (Brockelm. II p. 465). The present book Al-Fath fi)t-tadâwî min sunûf al-amrâd wa'sh-shakâwî is not mentioned by Brpckelm., but by Hadji Khalfa (ed. Fluegel) vol. IV p. 374 No. 8868. The copy has been made Ahmad al-Azharî (a pupil of the al-Azhar-School ?), probably in Cairo, in the ye/ar 1058/1648, conseqüently during the life-time of the author and 10 years before the completion of his afore-mentioned other work. So this copy has a particular value.

Max Meyerhof

to the RCP is evidenced by his *ex libris*, found on the front pastedown. Moreover, there is a letter from Max Meyerhof to Dobbin on Meyerhof's attractive bilingual stationary, in which Meyerhof writes:

> Abū Saᶜīd Ibrāhīm ibn Muḥammad al-Maghribī was a Moroccan or Algerian physician of the XVIIth century. Brockelmann knows of him a book on sexual intercourse written in 1068/1658 (Brockelm. II p465). The present book *Al-Fath fi't-tadāwī min sunūf al-amrād wa'shakāwī* is not mentioned by Brockelm., but by Hadji Khal[i] fa (ed Fluegel) vol. IV p.374 No. 8868. The copy has been made [by] Ahmad al-Azharī (a pupil of the al-Azhar-School?), probably in Cairo, in the year 1058/1648, consequently during the life-time of the author and 10 years before the completion of his afore-mentioned other work. So this copy has a particular value.

Meyerhof already realised the importance of this manuscript, as detailed above. By mentioning Brockelmann, he refers to the latter's *Geschichte der arabischen Literatur* in its first edition; in the second edition, Brockelmann does mention this text (1937–49), ii 465. Ḥāǧǧī Ḫalīfa (known as Kātip Čelebī, d 1657), whom Meyerhof mentioned, was a famous Ottoman intellectual who wrote an important bibliographical encyclopaedia called *Discovery of opinions about the names of books on various subjects* (*Kašf al-Ẓunūn ᶜan asāmī l-kutub wa-l-funūn*) in Arabic; it was edited by Flügel (1835–58). Our manuscript also contains a piece of paper on which Dobbin copied two sources for the life of the author: an Arabic extract from the work by the 19th-century scholar Muḥammad ibn Muḥammad Maḫlūf entitled *Tree of pure light about the generation of the Malikite school* (*Šağarat al-nūr al-zakīya fī ṭabaqāt al-Mālikīya*) and Flügel's Latin translation of the passages from the *Discovery of opinions* about this work, to which Meyerhof referred (Flügel 1835–58: vol iv, p374, no 8868). Dobbin then donated this manuscript on Meyerhof's behalf to the RCP.

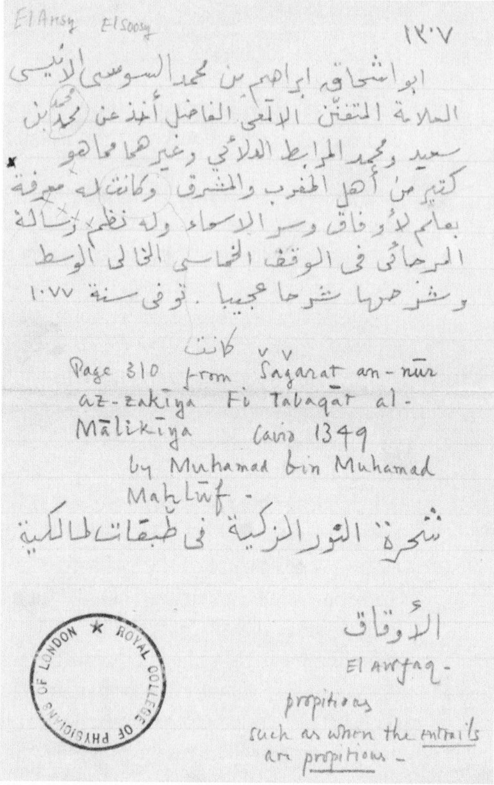

Fig 9.3, no 31 Roy Dobbin's notes on *Victory in the treatment of different types of diseases and complaints*, 20th century.

No 32 (MSTR59): Manuscript containing *Tales of the parrot*, donated by Dobbin

This manuscript contains the Persian translation of an Indian work known as the *Seventy tales of the parrot* (*Śukasaptati*). The story revolves around a merchant, his wife and a parrot under a spell. The merchant has given the parrot to his wife, but has to leave on a long journey. As time goes on, the wife grows wary and is tempted to take a lover. The parrot openly encourages her in this endeavour, whilst secretly spinning a plot to prevent this from happening. Each night, the parrot tells the wife a story that ends in a cliff-hanger and thus ensures that he only finishes after it is too late for the wife to go out. In the original, this pattern of storytelling and suspense continues for 69 nights, whereas it is only 51 in the Persian adaptation. When the husband finally comes home, he is displeased with the intentions of his wife, but the parrot tells one last tale and the couple reconcile. The Persian adaptation with 52 tales has the titles of *Ṭūṭīnāma*, literally *Book of the parrot* and was written by Ḍiyāʾ al-Dīn Naḫšabī (d 1350), about whom little is known. In many manuscripts, we find not only rich illuminations, but also considerable variations in the stories (Simsar 1978). We also have illuminations in the present manuscript, although they are not quite as fine as those found elsewhere.

This manuscript illustrates the fact that the RCP has a small number of non-medical Arabic and Persian manuscripts in its collections. Other examples include Arabic copies of the Koran (MSS Tritton 43–4) and Persian examples of calligraphy (MSS Tritton 61–2). The manuscript of the *Tales of the parrot* was donated to the RCP by Dobbin.

› No 33 (MSTR8): Modern Arabic manuscript of al-Badadī's work on gynaecology, obstetrics and childcare, copied in Cairo and donated by Dobbin

Abū l-ʿAbbās Aḥmad ibn Muḥammad ibn Yaḥyā al-Baladī is most noted for writing a book *On the therapy of pregnant women and children*. Little is known of his life, apart from the fact that he probably came from a village near Mosul, studied under the physician Ibn al-Ašʿaṯ in Mosul, lived many years in Egypt, and wrote his gynaecological work in 965 at the behest of his teacher and dedicated it to his patron Ibn Killis (d 990). The *Therapy of pregnant women and children* comprises three *maqālas* (books, sections), the first of which consists of 58 chapters (*bābs*) about embryology and obstetrics, the second of 48 chapters about treatment of infants, and the third of 61 chapters about children's diseases from tip to toe. In many cases, al-Baladī quotes previous authorities in his work; important sources of inspiration are the monographs entitled *Therapy of children* by Rufus of Ephesus (fl c100) and Paul of Aegina (fl 650s) (Pormann 2002).

The present manuscript was commissioned by Roy Dobbin and completed on Monday 11 Rabīʿ I AH 1355 (1 June AD 1936) by Maḥmūd Ṣidqī, a professional scribe at the Egyptian National Library (*Dār al-Kutub wa-l-waṯāʾiq al-qawmīya*). He copied the text from a 13th-century exemplar at the same library with the shelfmark MS 1803 Ṭibb, as we learn from the colophon on pages 552–3:

> The copying of this book was finished on the morning of Monday, 11 Rabīʿ I AH 1355, corresponding to 1 June AD 1936. It is based on a manuscript preserved in the Egyptian National Library, no 1803 ṭibb. The latter is the only manuscript of its type in the Egyptian National Library. This book was copied at the behest of Dr Roy Dobbin, the specialist in gynaecology and obstetrics, chief physician (*ḥakīm bāšā*) at the hospital *Qaṣr al-ʿAynī*, professor in the Egyptian medical faculty. It was copied by Maḥmūd Ṣidqī, the scribe, who hopes for the forgiveness of his lord, at the aforementioned Library. May God bless Him after whom there is no prophet [ie Muḥammad] and his family and companions, and grant them peace.

Dobbin thus had a work copied that was of direct interest to him, as it dealt with his specialities: gynaecology and obstetrics. In this he followed Max Meyerhof, who often commissioned modern handwritten copies of medieval medical manuscripts that were of relevance to him. A significant number of the latter are still preserved today at the Bibliotheca Alexandrina and the Egyptian National Library.

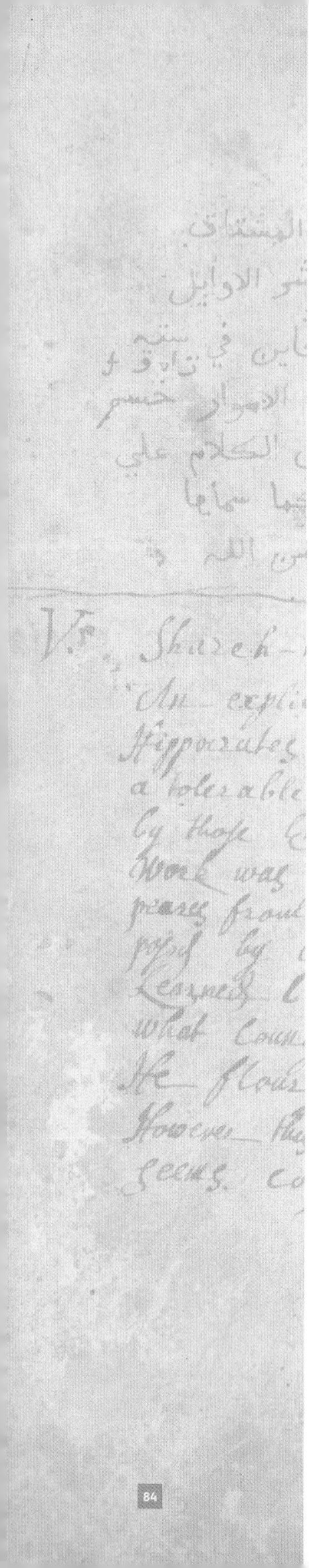

Conclusions

The introduction and the nine chapters above have shown that medicine in the Islamic world drew on the knowledge of previous civilisations, especially that of the Greeks, but also developed into a rich and sophisticated tradition in its own right. There are three main conclusions that we can draw from this short journey through some of the highlights in the Arabo-Islamic medical tradition.

First, in medicine as elsewhere, the Christian and the Muslim worlds have a common heritage. The fates and fortunes of physicians across the Mediterranean during the medieval period are intimately linked. They inhabited a shared epistemic space in which texts and ideas travelled across linguistic and confessional boundaries. Moreover, one cannot tell the story of this medical legacy in terms of torchbearers. That is to say, the Greeks did not bear the torch of medical science for a while, only to pass it on to the Arabs and Muslims, who in their turn relayed it to the Latin-speaking Christians. Rather, a complex web of bilateral and multilateral exchanges existed in which knowledge travelled through a variety of channels. James Montgomery (2007) rightly talked of crosspollination to describe this complex exchange of ideas.

Second, one cannot just see the role of Arab or Muslim physicians as that of transmitters, as some have done. The medical system that the Arabs and Muslims developed in the medieval period was full of innovation. Whether they discovered new diseases, distinguished between conditions that had previously been confused, discovered new treatments, developed new methods to test drugs, invented new instruments, organised medical knowledge in novel ways or illustrated human anatomy in unprecedented detail – medical practitioners operating in the pre-modern Islamic world displayed a high level of sophistication, again and again. Some innovations resulted directly from the new political, social, economic and geographical situation. Had it not been for the large and well endowed hospitals in which al-Rāzī worked, he could hardly have made statistical observations based on hundreds of patients. Through trade and travel, new drugs came onto the market and were exploited to the full by physicians. The availability of cheap paper also played a role in the development of a highly literate society, interested in many different cultures and religions.

Third, this vibrant medical culture did not come to a close because of religious bigotry or foreign invasion, as some have claimed. They allege – wrongly, it should be stated from the outset – that with al-Ġazālī (d 1111) religious orthodoxy triumphed over unfettered philosophical enquiry; and that the Mongols destroyed the material basis for scientific research, when they sacked Baghdad in 1258. Yet the works of later authors such as Ibn al-Nafīs, ʿAbd al-Laṭīf al-Baġdādī, Ibn Ilyās and Ibn Sallūm tell a different tale. They illustrate that medicine continued to develop as a discipline, and science and culture did not sink into the morass of moral turpitude or religious fanaticism. Already at the height of the ʿAbbāsid Empire, we find certain scholars who viewed what they labelled 'foreign learning' with suspicion; this did not, however, mean that most intellectuals rejected Greek ideas. On the contrary, the great polymath al-Kindī fervently argued that truth does not differ whether arrived at by Muslim or non-Muslim, and that one should therefore seek it from all civilisations (Adamson, Pormann 2012: 11). For him, the truth revealed by the prophets is the same as that to which philosophers have access; the latter only have to work much harder to attain it (Adamson, Pormann 2012: 286–7). Therefore, although we occasionally find tensions between religion and philosophy (of which the sciences were part), it is wrong to imagine that a 'decline and fall' in medical or other achievements was brought about by the onslaught of orthodoxy. The Islamic medical heritage is therefore rich and sophisticated on a number of levels. During the Renaissance and the early modern period, both physicians and the general public were still aware of this, as the RCP collections demonstrate. Yet, as Alain de Libera (1991) has shown for philosophy, this heritage has been largely forgotten, at least in certain circles. Even today, a prominent academic such as Andrew Cunningham can tell the history of Western medicine with virtually no reference to its Arabo-Islamic heritage – as he did in his 30-part radio programme with the title *The making of modern medicine*, produced by the BBC in collaboration with the Open University. Furthermore, pupils sometimes study the history of medicine in a similar way in schools.

'... although we occasionally find tensions between religion and philosophy ... it is wrong to imagine that a 'decline and fall' in medical or other achievements was brought about by the onslaught of orthodoxy ...'

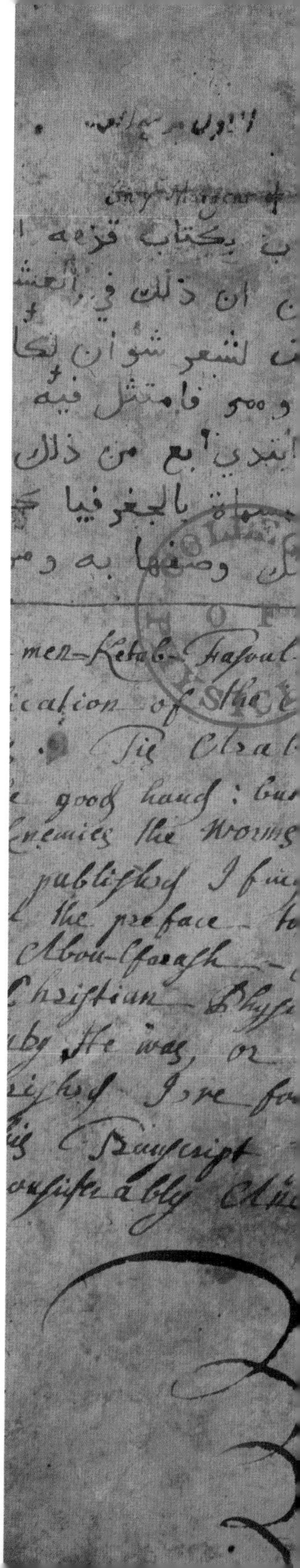

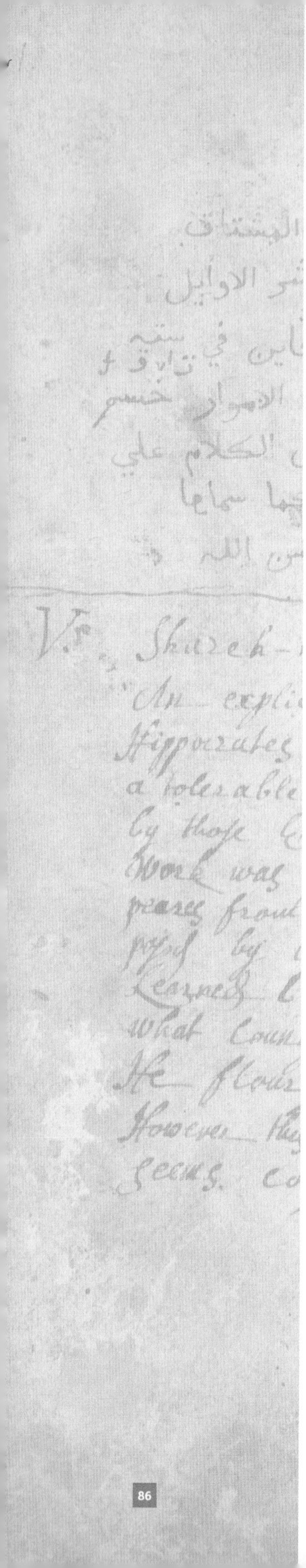

Alain de Libera argued that this amnesia is not an innocent one, but can be linked to ideas about racial and religious purity. For the Renaissance, this is certainly true: influential physicians such as Leonard Fuchs (1501–66) and others reduced the contribution of the Arabs to introducing errors (Pormann 2011c). Even today, this amnesia is associated with similar tendencies, as the controversy around Sylvain Gouguenheim illustrates. In 2008, Gouguenheim argued that medieval Islamic culture had hardly been touched by the Greek heritage, that the Arabic language was ill adapted to rational thought, and that Arabic translations only played a limited role in the transmission of Greek ideas to medieval Europe. Among the barrage of criticism that these ideas incurred, Büttgen *et al* (2009) rightly labelled Gouguenheim's position as 'scholarly islamophobia' (*islamophobie savante*). The rich heritage of the RCP and its special collections offer an important corrective to this perception: it provides a timely reminder that can dispel this amnesia.

We can only hope that in the future we will teach the history of this shared medical heritage. Kipling claimed that 'East is East and West is West, and never the twain shall meet'. Nothing could be further from the truth: the pre-modern history of the Islamic world in general and of medicine in particular shows innumerable instances of intellectual kinship, a kinship poignantly revealed through the collections of the Royal College of Physicians in London.

'... the pre-modern history of the Islamic world in general and of medicine in particular shows innumerable instances of intellectual kinship, a kinship poignantly revealed through the collections of the Royal College of Physicians in London.'

Note on transliteration and dates

Arabic and Persian words are transliterated here according to a system where one letter in the source language corresponds to one letter in the target language. For the most part, the English speaker can ignore these diacritical marks. For those who aim at a more accurate pronunciation, the following explanation may be useful.

ʾ marks a glottal stop, as in cockney *buʾa* for 'butter'. ʿ is technically speaking as 'voiced pharyngeal fricative' and has no equivalent in English, but can be approximated by a strong glottal stop. A dot underneath the consonants *ḍ*, *ṣ*, *ṭ*, *ẓ* means that they are pronounced in an emphatic way. The letters *ḏ* and *ṯ* should be pronounced as voiced and unvoiced English *th* respectively; in other words, *ḏ* corresponds to the *th* in 'the'; and *ṯ* to the *th* in 'thin'. Both *ḥ* and *ḫ* are stronger versions of aspirated *h*; the latter (*ḫ*) corresponds to the Scottish *ch* in 'loch' or the Scottish *gh* in the name 'Naughtie'. Moreover, š and ǧ represent the *sh* and *j* sounds, respectively; so *š* sounds like the *sh* in 'shine', and *ǧ* like the *g* in 'gin' or *j* in 'joke'. Finally, *ġ* denotes a French 'r', as in the word 'ratatouille'.

All dates, unless otherwise noted, correspond to the Christian era (AD), also called 'Common Era' (CE). The Muslim era is marked by the abbreviation AH, standing for 'Anno Hegirae' (in the year after the *hiǧra*). The *hiǧra*, that is, the Prophet Muḥammad's move (or 'flight') from Mecca to Medina, occurred in AD 622. Muslims, however, follow a lunar calendar, in which each year consists of 12 lunar months, each either 29 or 30 days long. Therefore, the Islamic year is only approximately 354 long, some 11 days shorter than the solar year. Therefore, the Islamic months are not linked to a specific time of year, as they recede every year by roughly 11 days. Therefore, the month of Ramaḍān, for instance, can fall in the middle of summer or in the middle of winter.

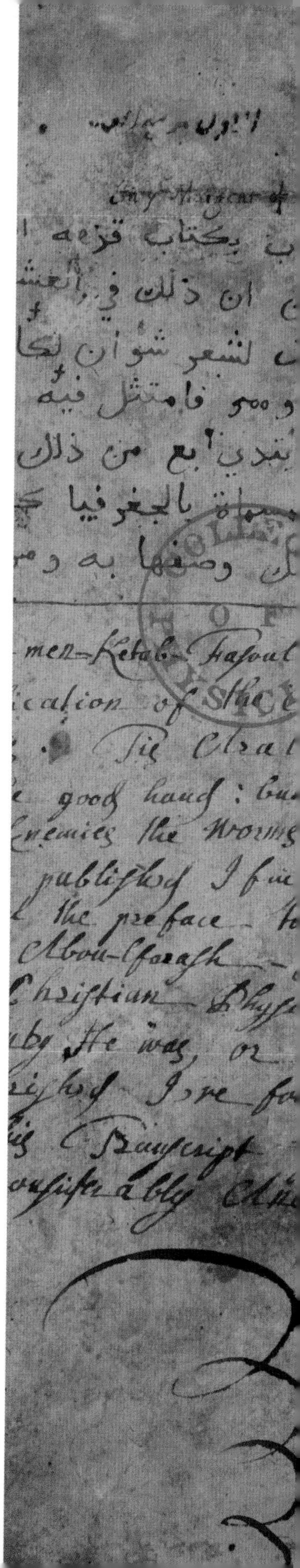

References

Adamson P (ed) (2013). *Interpreting Avicenna*. Cambridge: Cambridge University Press.

Adamson P (in preparation). *Abū Bakr al-Rāzī*. Oxford: Oneworld Press.

Adamson P, Pormann PE (2012). *The philosophical works of al-Kindī*. Karachi: Oxford University Press.

Akasoy AA, Yoeli-Tlalim R (2007). Along the musk routes: exchanges between Tibet and the Islamic world. *Asian medicine* 3:217–40.

Akasoy AA, Burnett C, Yoeli-Tlalim R (2008). *Astromedicine: astrology and medicine, East and West*. Micrologus Library. Florence: Sismel.

Akasoy AA, Montgomery JE, Pormann PE (eds) (2007). *Islamic crosspollinations: interactions in the medieval Middle East*. Oxford: Oxbow.

Álvarez-Millán C (2000). Practice versus theory: tenth-century case histories from the Islamic Middle East. In: Horden P, Savage-Smith E (eds), *The year 1000: medical practice at the end of the first millennium*, Social history of medicine 13.2. Oxford: Oxford University Press, 293–306; reprinted in Pormann 2011a:i, 283–98.

Álvarez-Millán C (2010). The case history in medieval Islamic medical literature: *Tajārib* and *Mujarrabāt* as source. *Medical history* 54:195–214.

Ambjörn L (2011). Book titles mentioned in the tenth-century medical encyclopedia *al-Muʿālağāt al-Buqrāṭīya*. *Galenos* 5:103–11.

Bachour N (2012). *Oswaldus Crollius und Daniel Sennert im frühneuzeitlichen Istanbul: Studien zur Rezeption des Paracelsismus im Werk des osmanischen Arztes Ṣāliḥ b. Naṣrullāh Ibn Sallūm al-Ḥalabī*. Freiburg: Centaurus-Verlag.

Bhayro S (2005). Syriac medical terminology: Sergius and Galen's Pharmacopia. *Aramaic Studies* 3:147–65.

Bhayro S, Hawley R, Kessel G, Pormann PE (2012). Collaborative research on the digital Syriac Galen palimpsest. *Semitica et Classica* 5:261–4.

Bhayro S, Hawley R, Kessel G, Pormann PE (2013). The Syriac Galen palimpsest: progress, prospects and problems. *Journal of Semitic Studies* 58:131–48.

Biesterfeldt HH (1973). *Galens Traktat 'Dass die Kräfte der Seele den Mischungen des Körpers folgen'. Abhandlungen zur Kunde des Morgenlandes* 40.4. Wiesbaden: Steiner.

Black WH (1845). *A descriptive, analytical, and critical catalogue of the manuscripts bequeathed unto the University of Oxford by Elias Ashmole, Esq, MD, FRS, Windsor Herald, also of some additional MSS. Contributed by Kinglsey, Lhuyd, Borlase and others*. Oxford.

Bray J (2006). The physical world and the writer's eye: al-Tānūkhī and medicine. In: Bray J (ed), *Writing and representation in medieval Islam: Muslim horizons*. London; New York: Routledge, Taylor & Francis Group, 215–49.

Brockelmann C (1937–49). *Geschichte der arabischen Litteratur*, vols 1–2 (2nd edn, Leiden: Brill, 1943–9), suppl vols 1–3 (Leiden: Brill 1937–42); reprinted 5 vols (Leiden: Brill, 1996).

Burnett C (2000). Antioch as a link between Arabic and Latin culture in the twelfth and thirteenth centuries. In: Draelants I, Tihon A, van den Abeele B (eds) *Occident et Proche-Orient: contacts scientifiques au temps des Croisades: actes du colloque de Louvain-la-Neuve, 24 et 25 mars 1997*. Turnhout: Brepols, 1–78; reprinted in Burnett 2009: item iv.

Burnett C (2009). *Arabic into Latin in the middle ages: the translators and their intellectual and social context*. Variorum Collected Studies series 939. Farnham: Ashgate/Variorum.

Büttgen P, de Libera A, Rashed M, Rosier-Catach I (eds) (2009). *Les grecs, les arabes et nous. Enquête sur l'islamophobie savant*. Paris: Fayard.

Chipman L (2002). How effective were cough remedies known to medieval Egyptians? *Koroth* 16:135–57; reprinted in Pormann 2011a:ii, 116–33.

Chipman L (2010). *The world of pharmacy and parmacists in Mamlūk Cairo*. Sir Henry Wellcome Asian Series, ns 8. Leiden: Brill.

Christianson P (2008). Selden, John (1584–1654), *Oxford dictionary of national biography*. Oxford: Oxford University Press, 2004; online edn, Jan 2008. www.oxforddnb.com/view/article/25052 [Accessed 14 February 2013].

Clark GN *et al* (1964–2005). *A history of the Royal College of Physicians of London*, 4 vols. Oxford: Clarendon Press for the Royal College of Physicians.

Conrad L *et al* (1995). *The western medical tradition: 800 BC to AD 1800*. Cambridge: Cambridge University Press.

Cooper GM (ed) (2011). *Galen, 'De Diebus Decretoriis', From Greek into Arabic: A critical edition, with translation and commentary, of Ḥunayn Ibn Isḥāq, 'Kitāb ayyām al-buḥrān'*. Medicine in the medieval Mediterranean. Farnham: Ashgate.

Daiber H (2012). Abū Bakr ar-Rāzī. In: Rudolph U (ed), *Grundriß der Geschichte der Philosophie, begründed von Friedrich Überweg. Philosophie in der Islamischen Welt*, vol 1. Basle: Schwabe Verlag, 261–89.

Dols MD (1992). *'Majnūn': The madman in medieval Islamic society*. Oxford: Clarendon Press.

Doufikar-Aerts F (2010). *Alexander Magnus Arabicus: a survey of the Alexander tradition through seven centuries: from pseudo-Callisthenes to Suri*, Mediaevalia Groningana, New Series 13. Leuven: Peeters.

Dueck JM (2010). *The claims of culture at empire's end: Syria and Lebanon under French rule.* Oxford: Oxford University Press/ British Academy.

Duffy JM (1984). Byzantine medicine in the sixth and seventh centuries: aspects of teaching and practice. In: Scarborough J (ed), *Symposium on Byzantine medicine*, Dumbarton Oaks Papers 38. Washington: 21–7.

Ebrahimnejad H (ed) (2009). *The development of modern medicine in non-western countries: historical perspectives.* London: Routledge.

Elgood CL (1962). Ṭibb-ul-Nabbi or medicine of the Prophet. *Osiris* 14:33–192.

Fancy N (2013). *Science and religion in Mamluk Egypt: Ibn al-Nafis, pulmonary transit and bodily resurrection.* London: Routledge.

Flügel G (1835–58). *Lexicon bibliographicum et encyclopædicum a Mustafa Ben Abdallah Katib Jelebi dicto et nomine Haji Khalfa celebrato compositum.* Leipzig: Published for the Oriental Translation Fund of Great Britain and Ireland.

Frede M (1985). *Three treatises on the nature of science.* Indianapolis, Ind: Hackett.

Gelvin JL (2008). *The modern Middle East: a history*, 2nd edn. New York: Oxford University Press.

Gourevitch D (1997). Un livre fantôme: Le Galien arabe de Greenhill. In: Jacquart D (ed), *Les voies de la science grecque: Études sur la transmission des textes de l'antiquité au dix-neuvième siècle*, Hautes Études Médiévales et Modernes 78. Geneva: Librairie Droz: 419–72.

Grabar O (1984). *The illustrations of the* Maqāmāt, *studies in medieval manuscript illumination.* Chicago Visual Library Text-fiche no.45. Chicago: University of Chicago Press.

Greenhill WA (1848). *A treatise on the small-pox and measles by Abú Becr Mohammed ibn Zacaríyá ar-Rází (commonly called Rhazes).* London. Reprinted Birmingham, Ala: Classics of Medicine Library, 1987.

Gutas D (1998). *Greek thought, Arabic culture: the Graeco-Arabic translation movement in Baghdad and early ʿAbbāsid society (2nd-4th/8th-10th Centuries)* London: Routledge.

Gutas D (2003). Medical theory and scientific method in the age of Avicenna. In Reisman DC (ed), *Before and after Avicenna: proceedings of the first conference of the Avicenna study group.* Islamic philosophy, theology and science: texts and studies 52. Leiden: Brill 145–62; reprinted in Pormann 2011a:i, 33–47.

Hampel J (1982). *Medizin der Zoroastrier im vorislamischen Iran.* Husum.

Hamilton A (2011). The Arcadian Library: *Western appreciation of Arab and Islamic civilisation.* Oxford: Arcadian Library in association with Oxford University Press.

Horden P (2008). *Hospitals and healing from antiquity to the later middle ages.* Collected Studies 881. Aldershot: Ashgate Variorum.

Horstmanshoff HFJ (2010). In collaboration with van Tilburg CR, *Hippocrates and medical education: selected papers read at the XIIth international Hippocrates colloquium, Universiteit Leiden, 24-26 August 2005.* Leiden: Brill.

Houtsma E (ed) (1881). Ibn al-ʿAnbārī, *Kitāb al-aḍdāḍ,: Kitābo'l-Adhdād sive Liber de vocabulis arabicis quae plures habent significationes inter se oppositas ...* Leiden.

Iskandar AZ. Ar-Rāzī, the clinical physician (*Ar-Rāzī al-ṭabīb al-Iklīnīkī*). In: Pormann 2011a:i, 207–53.

James MR (1907–8). *A descriptive catalogue of the manuscripts in the library of Gonville and Caius college*, 2 vols. Cambridge: Cambridge University Press.

Joosse NP, Pormann PE (2010). Decline and decadence in Iraq and Syria after the age of Avicenna? ʿAbd al-Laṭīf al-Baghdādī (1162–1231) between myth and history. *Bulletin of the history of medicine* 84:1–29.

Joosse NP, Pormann PE (2012). Commentaries on the Hippocratic aphorisms in the Arabic tradition: the example of melancholy. In: Pormann 2012a:211–249.

Kahl O (2009). *Sābūr ibn Sahl's dispensatory in the recension of the ʿAḍudī Hospital.* Leiden: Brill.

Ker NR (1969). *Medieval manuscripts in British libraries.* Oxford: Oxford University Press.

Klein-Franke F (1984). *Iatromathematics in Islam: a study on Yuhanna Ibn aṣ-Ṣalt's book on astrological medicine.* Hildesheim; New York: G. Olms.

Koetschet P (2011). La mélancolie chez al-Rāzī, entre médecine et philosophie, thèse de doctorat/PhD thesis. Université de Paris-Sorbonne, University of Warwick.

Leiser G (1983). Medical education in Islamic lands from the seventh to the fourteenth century. *Journal of the history of medicine and allied sciences* 38:48–75; reprinted in Pormann 2011a:ii, 161–184.

Leiser G, al-Khaledy N (2003). *Questions and answers for physicians: a medieval Arabic study manual by ʿAbd al-ʿAzīz al-Sulamī.* Sir Henry Wellcome Asian series 3. Leiden, Boston: Brill.

Lewis B (2002). *What went wrong.* London: Weidenfeld and Nicolson.

Libera A (1991). *Penser au Moyen-Âge.* Paris: Édition du Seuil.

Littré É (ed) (1839–61). *Œuvres complètes d'Hippocrate.* 10 vols. Paris.

Maddison F, Savage-Smith E (1997). *Science, tools and magic*, 2 vols. London: Nour Foundation in association with Azimuth Editions and Oxford University Press.

Meyerhof M (1935a). Thirty three clinical observations by Rhazes (circa 900 AD). *Isis* 23:321–56 and 14 pages of Arabic; reprinted in Meyerhof, *Studies in medieval Arabic medicine: theory and practice.* Johnstone P (ed), Variorum Reprints. London: Ashgate, 1984, item v.

Meyerhof M (1935b). Ibn An-Nafis (XIIIth century) and his theory of the lesser circulation. *Isis* 23:100–20.

Michot Y (2006). *Avicenne. Réfutation de l'astrologie.* Beyrouth: Les Éditions Al-Bouraq.

Montgomery J (2007). Islamic crosspollinations. In: Akasoy *et al* 2007:148–93.

Munday J (ed) (1809). *A selection of curious articles from the gentleman's magazine*, 3 vols. Oxford.

Nutton V (1987). *John Caius and the manuscripts of Galen.* Proceedings of the Cambridge Philological Society, suppl vol. 13. Cambridge: Cambridge Philological Society.

Nutton V (2012). Vesalius revised. His annotations to the 1555 *Fabrica. Medical history* 56:415–43.

Nutton V (2013). *Ancient medicine*, 2nd edn. London: Routledge.

Omrani A (ed) (2010). *Ishâq Ibn Imrân: traité de la mélancolie, Beït al-Hikma.* Tunis.

Overwien O (2005). *Die Sprüche des Kynikers Diogenes in der griechischen und arabischen Überlieferung.* Hermes Einzelschriften 92. Stuttgart: Franz Steiner.

Overwien O (2012) The art of the translator, or: how did Ḥunayn ibn ʾIsḥāq and his school translate? In: Pormann 2012a:151–70.

Paavilainen HM (2009). *Medieval pharmacotherapy - continuity and change*, Studies in ancient medicine 38. Leiden: Brill.

Paulet J-J (1768). *Histoire de la petite vérole ...* Paris: Chez Ganeau.

Perho I (1995). *The Prophet's medicine: a creation of the Muslim traditionalist scholars*, Studia Orientalia 74. Helsinki: Finnish Oriental Society.

Pormann PE (2002). The Greek and Arabic fragments of Paul of Aegina's *Therapy of children.* MPhil thesis, Oxford University; available at: http://ora.ox.ac.uk/objects/uuid:65f039b9-d4d3-4c44-9db5-e4e593f31006 [Accessed 21 February 2013].

Pormann PE (2003). Theory and practice in the early hospitals in Baghdad — al-Kaškarī on rabies and melancholy. *Zeitschrift für Geschichte der Arabisch-Islamischen Wissenschaften* 15:197–248.

Pormann PE (2004a). *The oriental tradition of Paul of Aegina's Pragmateia*, Studies in ancient medicine 29. Leiden: Brill.

Pormann PE (2004b). The Alexandrian summary (*Jawāmiʿ*) of Galen's *On the sects for beginners*: commentary or abridgment? In: Adamson P *et al* (eds), *Philosophy, science and exegesis in Greek, Arabic and Latin commentaries. Bulletin of the Institute of Classical Studies.* Supplement 83, 2 vols. London ii. 11–33.

Pormann PE (2004c). Yuḥannā ibn Sarābiyūn: further studies into the transmission of his works. *Arabic sciences and philosophy* 14:233–62.

Pormann PE (2005). The physician and the other: images of the charlatan in medieval Islam. *Bulletin of the history of medicine* 79:189–227; reprinted in Pormann 2011a:ii, 203–239.

Pormann PE (2007a). Islamic medicine crosspollinated: a multilingual and multiconfessional maze. In: Akasoy *et al* 2007:76–91.

Pormann PE (2007b). Al-Rāzī (d. 925) on the benefits of sex: a clinician caught between philosophy and medicine. In: Vrolijk A, Hogendijk JP (eds), *O ye gentlemen: Arabic studies on science and literary culture, in honour of Remke Kruk.* Leiden [etc]: Brill, 115–127; reprinted in Pormann 2011a: ii, 134–145.

Pormann PE (ed) (2008a). *Rufus of Ephesus on melancholy.* SAPERE 12, Tübingen: Mohr Siebeck.

Pormann PE (2008b). Case notes and clinicians: Galen's commentary on the Hippocratic *epidemics* in the Arabic tradition. *Arabic sciences and philosophy* 18:247–84.

Pormann PE (2008c). Medical methodology and hospital practice: the case of tenth-century Baghdad. In: Adamson P (ed), *In the age of al-Farabi: Arabic philosophy in the 4th/10th century.* Warburg Institute Colloquia 12. London: Warburg Institute: 95–118.

Pormann PE (2008d). *Ibn Sarābiyūn: ṭabīb ʿalā muftaraq ṭuruq al-ḥaḍārāt bayna l-šarq wa-l-ġarb* (Ibn Serapion: a physician at the crossroads of cultures between East and West). *al-Mašriq* 82:343–59.

Pormann PE (2009a). Female patients and practitioners in medieval Islam. *The Lancet* 373:1598–9.

Pormann PE (2009b). Al-Kaskarī (10th cent.) and the quotations of classical authors: a philological study. In: Garofalo I, Lami A, Roselli A (eds), *Sulla tradizione indiretta dei testi medici greci: atti del II seminario internazionale di Siena Certosa di Pontignano, 19–20 settembre 2008*, Biblioteca di «Galenos» 2. Pisa, Rome: F. Serra, 107–39.

Pormann PE (2010a). Medical education in late antiquity: from Alexandria to Montpellier. In: Horstmanshoff 2010:419–41.

Pormann PE (2010b). Arabic astronomy and the Copernican 'revolution', review article of George Saliba. *Islamic science and the making of the European Renaissance.* London: Cambridge, Mass: MIT Press, 2007. In: *Annals of science* 67:243–8.

Pormann PE (2010c) Islamic hospitals in the time of al-Muqtadir. In: John Nawas (ed), *Abbasid studies II: occasional papers of the school of ʿAbbasid studies, Leuven, 28 June–1 July 2004.* Orientalia Lovaniensia Analecta 177, Leuven; Dudley, Mass: Peeters, 337–82; reprinted in 2011b:i, 136–78.

Pormann PE (ed) (2011a). *Islamic medical and scientific tradition.* Critical concepts in Islamic studies, 4 vols. Routledge: London.

Pormann PE (2011b). The formation of the Arabic pharmacology: between tradition and innovation. *Annals of Science* 68:493–515.

Pormann PE (2011c). The dispute between the philarabic and philhellenic physicians and the forgotten heritage of Arabic medicine. In: Pormann 2011a:ii, 283–316.

Pormann PE (ed) (2012a). *Epidemics in context: Greek commentaries on Hippocrates in the Arabic tradition.* Scientia Graeco-Arabica 8, Berlin: De Gruyter.

Pormann PE (2012b). The development of translation techniques from Greek into Syriac and Arabic: the case of Galen's *On the faculties and powers of simple drugs*, Book Six. In: Hansberger R, Afifi al-Akiti M, Burnett C (eds), *Medieval Arabic thought: essays in honour of Fritz Zimmermann*. London: Warburg Institute; Turin: Nino Aragno Editore, 143–62.

Pormann PE (2013a). Avicenna on medical practice, epistemology, and the physiology of the inner senses. In: Adamson 2013:91–108.

Pormann PE (2013b). Medical epistemology and melancholy: Rufus of Ephesus and Miskawayh. In: Harris WV (ed), *Mental disorders in the classical world*. Columbia studies in the classical tradition 38, Leiden: Brill, 223–43.

Pormann PE (2013c). Qualifying and quantifying medical uncertainty in 10th century Baghdad: Abū Bakr al-Rāzī. *JLL Bulletin*: Commentaries on the history of treatment evaluation (www.jameslindlibrary.org).

Pormann PE (2014). New fragments from Rufus of Ephesus' on melancholy. *Classical Quarterly* [forthcoming].

Pormann PE, Savage-Smith E (2007). *Medieval Islamic medicine. New Edinburgh Islamic surveys*. Edinburgh: Edinburgh University Press.

Rosenthal F (1966). 'Life is short, the art is long': Arabic commentaries on the first Hippocratic aphorism. *Bulletin of the history of medicine* 40:226–45.

Saliba G (1994). *A history of Arabic astronomy: planetary theories during the golden age of Islam*. New York: New York University Press.

Saliba G (2007). *Islamic science and the making of the European Renaissance*. London: Cambridge, Mass: MIT Press.

Šams al-Dīn al-Ḏahabī (1996). *Al-Ṭibb al-nabawī li-l-Ḥāfiẓ al-Ḏahabī (Prophetic Medicine by the Ḥāfiẓ al-Dhahabī)*. Cairo: Maktabat Nizār Muṣṭafā al-Bāz.

Savage-Smith E (1980). Ibn al-Nafīs's *Perfected book on ophthalmology* and his treatment of trachoma and its sequelae. *Journal for the history of Arabic science* 4:147–204; reprinted in Pormann 2011a:ii, 36–98.

Savage-Smith E (1987). Drug therapy of eye diseases in seventeenth-century Islamic medicine: the influence of the 'new chemistry' of the Paracelsians. *Pharmacy in history* 29:3–28.

Savage-Smith E (1988). John Channing: eighteenth-century apothecary and Arabist. *Pharmacy in history* 30:63–80.

Savage-Smith E (1995). Attitudes toward dissection in medieval Islam. *Journal of the history of medicine and allied sciences* 50:67–110; reprinted in Pormann 2011a:i, 299–342.

Savage-Smith E (1999). The exchange of medical and surgical ideas between Europe and Islam. In: Greppin *et al* (eds), *Diffusion of Greco-Roman medicine into the Middle East and the Caucasus*. Delmar, NY: Caravan Books, 27–55.

Savage-Smith E (2000). The practice of surgery in Islamic lands: myth and reality. In: Horden P, Savage-Smith E, *The year 1000: medical practice at the end of the first millennium. Social history of medicine* 13.2, Oxford: Oxford University Press, 307–21.

Savage-Smith E (2002). Galen's lost ophthalmology and the *Summaria Alexandrinorum*. In: Nutton V (ed), *The unknown Galen. Bulletin of the Institute of classical studies, Suppl 77*. London, 121–38.

Savage-Smith E (ed) (2004). *Magic and divination in early Islam*. The formation of the classical Islamic world 42. London: Ashgate.

Savage-Smith E (2007). Anatomical illustration in Arabic manuscripts. In: Contadini A (ed), *Arab painting: text and image in illustrated Arabic manuscripts*. Boston: Brill, 147–160; reprinted in Pormann 2011a:ii, 185–202.

Savage-Smith E (2011). *A new catalogue of Arabic manuscripts in the Bodleian Library, University of Oxford. Vol I: Medicine*. Oxford: Oxford University Press.

Savage-Smith E (2012), 'The Working Files of Rhazes: Are the *Jāmiʿ* and the *Ḥāwī* Identical?', in: *Medieval Arabic Thought: Essays in Honour of Fritz Zimmermann*, ed. R. Hansberger, M. Afifi al-Akiti, Ch. Burnett (London: Warburg Institute; Turin: Nino Aragno Editore), 163–80.

Scarborough J (2010). Teaching surgery in late Byzantine Alexandria. In: Horstmanshoff 2010:235–60.

Sezgin F (1970). *Medizin-Pharmazie-Zoologie-Tierheilkunde bis ca 430 H.*, Geschichte des arabischen Schrifttums 3. Leiden: Brill.

Sezgin F (ed) (1986). *Augenheilkunde im Islam: Texte, Studien und Übersetzungen*, 4 vols. Frankfurt: Institut für Geschichte der Arabisch-Islamischen Wissenschaften.

Shefer Mossensohn M (2009). *Ottoman medicine*. New York: State University of New York Press.

Shefer Mossensohn M (2011). An Ottoman physician and his social and intellectual milieu: the case of Salih bin Nasrallah Ibn Sallum. *Studia Islamica* 1:133–58 [available at www.studiaislamica.com/pdf/2011-1/Shefer.pdf].

Selden J (1642). *Eutychii Aegyptii patriarchae orthodoxorum Alexandrini, scriptoris, ut in Oriente admodùm vetusti ac illustris, ita in Occidente tum paucissimis visi tum perraró auditi, ecclesiae suae originis*. London: Richard Bishop.

Siggel A (1951). *Die indischen Bücher aus dem Paradies der Weisheit über die Medizin des Ali ibn Sahl Rabban at-Tabari*. Abhandlungen der Geistes- und Sozialwissenschaftlichen Klasse 1950, no. 14. Mainz: Verlag der Akademie der Wissenschaften und der Literatur. F. Steiner: Wiesbaden.

Šihāda K (ed) (1997). *al- Ṭibb al-ǧadīd al-kīmīyāʾī li-Ṣāliḥ Naṣr Allāh ibn Sallūm al-Ḥalabī*. Aleppo: Ǧāmiʿat Ḥalab, Maʿhad al-Turāṯ al-ʿIlmī al-ʿArabī.

Simsar MA (ed and tr) (1978). *Tales of a parrot - The Cleveland Museum of Art's Ṭūṭīnāma*. Cleveland: The Museum.

Siraisi NG (1987). *Avicenna in Renaissance Italy: the canon and the medical teaching in Italian universities after 1500.* Princeton: Princeton University Press.

Siraisi NG (2001). *Medicine and the Italian universities, 1250-1600.* Leiden: Brill.

Siraisi NG (2007). *History, medicine, and the traditions of Renaissance learning.* Ann Arbor: University of Michigan Press.

Strohmaier G (2012). Galen the Pagan and Ḥunayn the Christian: specific transformations in the commentaries on *Airs, waters, places* and the *Epidemics.* In: Pormann 2012a:171–184.

Temkin O (1973). *Galenism: rise and decline of a medical philosophy.* Ithaca NY: Cornell University Press.

Thornton JL, Want PC (1974). Roy Samuel Dobbin (1873–1939). In: *Proceedings of the XXIII international congress of the history of medicine.* London, ii:1087–98.

Tibi S (2006). *The medicinal use of opium in ninth-century Baghdad.* Sir Henry Wellcome Asian Series 5, Leiden: Brill.

Toomer GJ (2008). Castell, Edmund (bap. 1606, d. 1686). *Oxford dictionary of national biography.* Oxford: Oxford University Press, 2004; online edn, 2008 www.oxforddnb.com/view/article/4865 [Accessed 14 February 2013].

Totelin L (2004). Mithradates' antidote: a pharmacological ghost. *Early Science and Medicine* 9:1–19.

Tritton AS (1951). Catalogue of oriental manuscripts in the library of the Royal College of Physicians. *Journal of the Royal Asiatic Society of Great Britain and Ireland*, 3/4:182–92.

Ullmann M (1970). *Die Medizin im Islam*, Handbuch der Orientalistik, I Abt. Erg. vi. 1, Leiden: Brill.

Ullmann M (1972). *Die Natur- und Geheimwissenschaften im Islam*, Handbuch der Orientalistik, I Abt. Erg. vi. 2, Leiden: Brill.

Ullmann M (1978). *Islamic medicine.* Islamic surveys 11. Edinburgh: Edinburgh University Press.

Ullmann M (2002). *Wörterbuch zu den griechisch-arabischen Übersetzungen des 9. Jahrhunderts.* Wiesbaden: Harrassowitz.

Ullmann M (2006). *Wörterbuch zu den griechisch-arabischen Übersetzungen des 9. Jahrhunderts.* Suppl I: A bis O, Wiesbaden: Harrassowitz.

Ullmann M (2007). *Wörterbuch zu den griechisch-arabischen Übersetzungen des 9. Jahrhunderts.* Suppl II: Π bis Ω, Wiesbaden: Harrassowitz.

Ullmann M (2009). *Untersuchungen zur arabischen Überlieferung der Materia medica des Dioskurides.* Wiesbaden: Harrassowitz.

Ullmann M (2011) *Die Nikomachische Ethik des Aristoteles in arabischer Übersetzung. Teil 1: Wortschatz.* Wiesbaden: Harrassowitz.

Ullmann M (2012) *Die Nikomachische Ethik des Aristoteles in arabischer Übersetzung. Teil 2: Überlieferung, Textkritik, Grammatik.* Wiesbaden: Harrassowitz.

Vagelpohl U (2011). In the translator's workshop. In: *Arabic sciences and philosophy* 21:249–88.

van Bladel K (2004). Hermes Arabicus. PhD dissertation, Yale University.

van Bladel K (2009) *The Arabic Hermes.* Oxford: Oxford University Press.

Veit R (2006). Der Arzt Andrea Alpago und sein medizinisches Umfeld im mamlukischen Syrien. *Miscellanea Mediaevalia* 33:305–16.

Waines D (1999). Dietetics in medieval Islamic culture. *Medical history* 43:228–40; reprinted in Pormann 2011a:ii, 99–115.

Webster C (2008). *Paracelsus: medicine, magic and mission at the end of time.* New Haven: Yale University Press.

Weston M (2003). Book of the month June 2003. At http://special.lib.gla.ac.uk/exhibns/month/june2003.html

Wootton D (2007). *Bad medicine: doctors doing harm since Hippocrates.* Oxford: Oxford University Press.

Zand KH, Videan JA and IE (1964). *The eastern key: Kitāb al-Ifādah wa-l-iʿtibār of ʿAbd al-Laṭīf al-Baghdādī* [The book of instruction and admonition ... Translated into English by...]. Cairo and London: George Allen and Unwin Ltd, 1964.